The Behaviour Management TOOLKIT

Margaret Sutherland
Colin Sutherland

Hodder & Stoughton
A MEMBER OF THE HODDER HEADLINE GROUP

Acknowledgements

In writing this book, we have discussed ideas and sought advice from many people. We would, however, like to acknowledge the particular contributions made by:

The SSA Team at St. Cecilia's RC High School, Longridge, Lancashire: **Chris Mason, Claudine Slowe, Diane Brewer, Sue White, Sue Hornyak** and **Ann Seed**. **Liz Locke** – Behaviour Support Teacher at Moorpark High School, Preston. **Janet Deakin** – Connexions Advisor, former Head Teacher of Ribbleton Hall High School, Preston.

Orders: please contact Bookpoint Ltd, 130 Milton Park, Abingdon, Oxon OX14 4SB. Telephone: (44) 01235 827720. Fax: (44) 01235 400454. Lines are open from 9.00 – 6.00, Monday to Saturday, with a 24 hour message answering service. You can also order through our website www.hodderheadline.co.uk

British Library Cataloguing in Publication Data
A catalogue record for this title is available from the British Library

ISBN 0 340 81464 0

First published 2004
Impression number   10 9 8 7 6 5 4 3 2 1
Year   2010 2009 2008 2007 2006 2005 2004

Copyright © 2004 Margaret Sutherland and Colin Sutherland

All rights reserved. This work is copyright. Permission is given for copies to be made of pages provided they are used exclusively within the institution for which this work has been purchased. For reproduction for any other purpose, permission must first be obtained in writing from the publishers.

Papers used in this book are natural, renewable and recyclable products. They are made from wood grown in sustainable forests. The logging and manufacturing processes conform to the environmental regulations of the country of origin.

Artwork by Oxford Designers and Illustrators.
Cover photo from Taxi/Getty Images.
Typeset by Fakenham Photosetting Limited, Fakenham, Norfolk.
Printed in Great Britain for Hodder & Stoughton Educational, a division of Hodder Headline, 338 Euston Road, London NW1 3BH by Hobbs the Printers Ltd, Hampshire.

Contents

Introduction	1
How to Use this Book	2
Useful Worksheets for All Units	3
Newsflashes	4
Changes	6
Helping _____ to be a Winner	7
Progress and Maintenance Log	8
Certificate for completing a course on _____	9

Unit 1 – Changing Classroom Behaviour — 10
Tutor Notes – Introduction	11
Section 1 **Preparing for Change**	12
Section 2 **Changing Behaviour**	18
Section 3 **Back-up Skills**	34

Unit 2 – Conflict Resolution — 41
Tutor Notes – Introduction	42
Section 4 **About Conflict Resolution**	44
Section 5 **Everyone's a Winner**	51
Section 6 **Skills for Conflict Resolution**	60

Unit 3 – Anger Management — 70
Tutor Notes – Introduction	71
Section 7 **Dealing with an Angry Child**	74
Section 8 **Assessing the Anger**	77
Section 9 **Basic Programme 1**	79
Section 10 **Basic Programme 2**	88
Section 11 **Basic Programme 3**	92
Section 12 **Additional Worksheets**	96

Unit 4 – Peer Relationships	106
Tutor Notes – Introduction	107
Section 13 Relationships	108
Section 14 Friends	114
Section 15 What is Bullying?	123
Section 16 Dealing with Bullying	131
Section 17 Bullies Can Change	142
Section 18 Peer Pressure	148

Unit 5 – Mood Management	152
Tutor Notes – Introduction	153
Section 19 Hearing Your Inner Voice	155
Section 20 Thinking, Feeling, Acting	162
Section 21 Manage That Mood	173
Section 22 Self-Esteem	178

Bibliography and References	**187**

Introduction

Many schools today still rely on traditional methods of rewards and penalties to control pupils' behaviour. In the short term and with less serious problems, these can be effective. However, there are increasing numbers of pupils for whom this sort of approach is inadequate.

The Behaviour Management Toolkit offers a radically different approach to altering behaviour. It seeks to motivate pupils to change and control their *own* behaviour rather than relying on external influences. To do this it provides them with 'tools' that fit into four categories:

1. Cognitive Tools – *'The way we think influences the way we feel and act'*

In the 1960s two psychologists Albert Ellis and Aaron T. Beck, working independently, broke away from the then mainstream areas of psychotherapy when they realised that the way their patients were thinking was a major cause of the depression from which they were suffering. Their research gave birth to a branch of Cognitive Psychology. Since then a wide body of research has extended this simple concept *'the way we think influences the way we feel and act'* into all areas of behaviour management.

2. Self-awareness Tools

Linked in with this cognitive approach is the development of 'self-awareness'. That is the understanding of our own thoughts and actions and where they are leading us. This can be a revelation to an adult. To a young person it can be very challenging and so needs to be handled sensitively.

3. Mind–body Tools

There is a tendency for all of us to consider mind–body relationships as one way. We accept that the brain controls the activities of our body but often fail to realise that what goes on in our body feeds back and influences the way our brain is working. For instance, simple procedures like slowing down the rate of breathing and relaxing certain muscles has the effect of calming an anxious or an angry mind, while changing body posture can influence our mood.

4. Imagination Tools

Psychotherapists regularly use the imagination of their clients to bring about changes of thinking and mood. For instance, rehearsing a difficult task in our imagination can help us to carry out that task more effectively. The imagination can also be used in an empathetic way, that is 'to put ourselves into someone else's shoes'. Using the imagination is a truly wonderful ability because there are no limits in the imagination. It is the tool that most of us use to motivate ourselves.

These four 'tools' are used throughout this book. In the worksheets accompanying each unit they will be explained in greater depth and made relevant to the particular behaviour change being sort.

How to Use this Book

The main practical tool used throughout this book is a pupil worksheet. Tutor notes at the start of each section explain the concepts being used while each worksheet has a brief instruction for use. There are also a few tutor worksheets.

As a tutor dealing with behavioural problems you will be carrying out work that, in the past, was done by specialist referral teams. It is essential, therefore, that you first understand the theory behind the procedures adopted in this book.

It is important to read all the tutor notes and the pupil worksheets selected before using them with a particular pupil. Do not expect the pupil to work through on his or her own. Work through each sheet together. In many cases you may need to scribe for him or her. This working together will help to establish the good rapport that is essential in what is a therapeutic relationship.

The way in which this toolkit is used will vary according to how much time is available to work with pupils. We suggest that the following ways could be considered.

1. **High access to pupils:** This will enable one-to-one work perhaps by SENCOs, SSAs (School Support Assistants), teachers in pupil referral units or teachers with time allocated for dealing with emotional/behavioural problems. We would suggest a minimum of one session per week over half a term followed up by regular maintenance sessions.

2. **Some access to pupils:** This will again be one-to-one work, with selective use of worksheets relevant to the particular pupil's problems. Perhaps this could involve pastoral staff with guidance from the SENCO.

3. **Small group work (3 to 4 pupils):** Certain worksheets lend themselves to small group work. For instance, issues relating to bullying, the nature of conflict and anger could be used in this way.

4. **Staff training:** The tutor notes and selected worksheets can also be used for staff training sessions. This will allow other staff to support maintenance programmes of pupils who have been through one of the behaviour change courses.

5. **Peer counselling:** With guidance, peer counsellors could use some worksheets. In the initial trials of the material certain worksheets were used this way with some success.

Changing behaviour is often a slow process. One trip through a few worksheets may make a transitory change, but it is unlikely to be permanent. Understanding and changing behaviour is like learning any academic subject, it will need constant reinforcement.

Sometimes you will find quite dramatic changes of behaviour, but beware of being complacent about such changes. A maintenance programme to ensure that the change becomes permanent is still necessary.

Useful Worksheets for All Units

Certain worksheets can be used alongside any of those in the five units of the Toolkit.

Two **newsflashes** are included. The first is intended to let people know that the student has agreed to start work on a particular unit. Discuss with the student who this should be sent to. Parents/carers, year heads and form teachers are obvious possible recipients. The second newsflash can be used during the course to let people know about particular achievements.

Changes can be used on a regular basis to review progress. This might be at the start of each session or just periodically, as required.

Helping _____ to be a winner is intended as a monitor of progress within the classroom. Targets need to be initially agreed with the student and then should be written into the first column (My Targets). The length of time for which the monitoring will take place needs to be decided and after that, sufficient copies of the worksheet should be photocopied. The monitor will give the student regular feedback during the day and other members of staff may become involved in supporting agreed changes. Subject teachers are required to tick, as appropriate, targets achieved in their lessons. Overall results should be discussed on a regular basis either with the tutor or with members of the pastoral staff. Although the monitor is particularly pertinent to the work covered in Unit 1 (Changing Classroom Behaviour), it may also be useful alongside other units in the Toolkit.

Finally, the **Progress and Maintenance Log** is intended so that tutors and students can keep track of the materials used and also record their feelings about the level of progress being made.

Just to let you know that

----

is taking part in a course on

Signed _____ Date _____

Just to let you know that

Signed _____ Date _____

Changes

Since our last session, these things are better:

Who else has noticed that things are better? How?

These things are still a problem:

Who else has noticed these problems? How?

Helping _____ to be a Winner

Please tick if the targets have been reached

	Lesson							
Date _____ My Targets ↓ ↓								
Teacher's initials								
Comments								

Progress and Maintenance Log

Name: _____ Form: _____

Date	Sections / Worksheets covered	Tutor comments on progress	Pupil comments on progress

Certificate for completing a course on

Awarded to

Signed   **Date**

© Hodder & Stoughton Ltd 2004. Copying permitted in purchasing school only.

Unit 1
Changing Classroom Behaviour

Tutor Notes – Introduction

Structure of the Course

The course is in three sections. The first, **Preparing for Change**, is about motivation and establishing a strong link between the pupil's dreams and ambitions and his/her education. Section 2, **Changing Behaviour**, puts forward an understanding of behaviour that includes not just actions but the accompanying thoughts and feelings. It goes on to develop an understanding of how thought processes influence feelings and actions. The fact that it is possible to choose to think differently is a crucial aspect of the student's own self-awareness. The final section, **Back-up Skills**, is about developing awareness of critical moments and how to deal with them.

Motivation

When a pupil has been referred to this programme because of poor classroom behaviour, it means that the teachers have been unable to motivate that pupil to change. This can happen despite every effort by teachers. They can make the lessons interesting. They can use a system of rewards and punishments to gain compliance. But when these do not work, the problem lies not with the teacher but with the internal thought processes of the pupil. For some reason, the pupil is thinking that this lesson is of no importance to him/her whatsoever. He or she may even be thinking, 'school is of no importance'.

However, that pupil will almost inevitably have dreams about where they want to be later in life and it is those dreams that must be accessed if motivation is to be developed. Furthermore a connection needs to be established between his/her education and the achievement of those dreams.

Changing Behaviour

Once the connection between dreams and education has been established, the pupil will need help changing what may be well-established behaviour patterns. This will involve looking at thought patterns in particular situations and getting the pupil to realise that thought processes influence behaviour.

Developing Self-awareness

Much of the rest of this unit is about developing self-awareness. The pupil needs to become aware of where his/her thoughts are leading. This awareness needs to be coupled with the realisation that it is possible to think differently.

Monitoring Change

At the end of Section 2, worksheets for helping pupils to monitor changes in their own behaviour are provided. This links in with the concept of developing self-awareness.

Section 1 Preparing for Change

The main objective of this section is to get the pupil to recognise the value of his/her education.

Notes for Pupil Worksheets
(You may need to scribe for the pupil)

Ups and Downs is a simple way of starting out and will provide an overall picture of the pupil's feelings about school. After this has been filled in, spend some time discussing the responses. It will enable you to understand things from the pupil's viewpoint and help to establish a rapport.

Timeline: there are many ways of motivating people to do things. Rewards, punishments and appeals to duty and loyalty will almost certainly have been tried without the desired result. The motivator used in this worksheet is ambition. We all have dreams about where we will be and what we will be doing in the future. Timeline therefore uses the pupil's dreams for the future as a motivator for change. It establishes a connection between the achievement of those dreams and his/her present education. It is important to remember that motivation needs to come from within. Lecturing the pupil on the importance of education for a career is likely to be counter-productive. The careful use of questions like "So if you want to be a mechanic in 5 years' time, what course do you need to get on at college?" will nudge the pupil's thoughts in the right direction.

When using Timeline, it is essential for students themselves to make the connection between their dreams for the future and their education. Education then becomes a central issue in their lives. However, at each stage in the time journey, get students to say *how they would feel* when their dreams are actually achieved. By doing this you can help them to embed a feeling of success.

Think About Consequences establishes the idea that all actions have consequences. The easiest to recognise are those that happen soon after a particular action. Long-term consequences are often harder to spot, but can have a very significant effect on the pupil's future options in life.

Looking Into My Future asks the pupil to think about the implications of their current behaviour and whether it fits in with their aspirations for the future. As well as providing students with some personal insight, this worksheet will also reinforce the motivation for change.

My Quality World is derived from the work of William Glasser. It consists of the people close to us; the possessions that we want to own; the things we like doing; the places we want to be and the ideas or beliefs that guide our behaviour. We tend to be happy when the real world in which we live matches or coincides with our quality world. Earlier worksheets have already established the pupil's dreams for the future and the role that education has in making this part of the real world. So it's now important to help them to recognise that *their quality world needs to include their education*.

1.1 Ups and Downs

Let's make a start by understanding how you feel about school.
If 10 is 'brilliant' and 0 is 'terrible', give school your score by marking it on the line below.

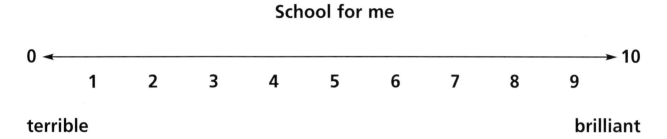

You probably decided that some things at school are OK. Perhaps you enjoy meeting your friends or possibly you like particular lessons. Maybe you like the lunches or the fact that you get to play football at break. Whatever your reasons, write down these OK things on the smiley face.

Other things will not be working out for you. On the sad face write down things that you don't like about school.

1.2 Timeline

Below is a timeline. Where it says 'Now', write your age and write (or draw) a few things in the box that represent your life **now**. After that, move on to where it says '5 years' time'. Write what your age will be and write (or draw) some things that show how you would **like** your life to be in 5 years' time. Explain your ideas to your tutor. How would you **feel** if you achieved your goals? Fill in the other boxes in the following order: 4 years' time, 3 years' time, 2 years' time, next year. Again explain each one to your tutor.

Age ↑

5 years' time

4 years' time

3 years' time

2 years' time

Next year

Now

1.3 Think About Consequences

Have you ever thrown a stone into a pond and watched the ripples spread out from where the stone hit the water? When you do something, your actions have **consequences** that ripple out around you, just like the stone in the water.

Some consequences are immediate. Here's an example:

Action	Immediate Consequence
Vernon throws a rubber across the classroom.	The teacher warns Vernon about his behaviour.

Think of some things you have done that have had immediate consequences. Write about them below.

Action	Immediate Consequence

Some consequences are long-term. You feel their effects later. Here's an example of a long-term consequence:

Action	Long-term Consequence
Helen always messes around with her mates in science.	She gets poor marks for science in her final exams. Helen is unable to get onto a college hairdressing course because her science grade is too low.

Think of some things you have done that have had long-term consequences. Write about them below.

Action	Long-term Consequence

1.4 Looking Into My Future

In the table below, write about your life in school at the moment. Include the good and the not so good things. Think about some of your actions. What are their immediate consequences? What do you think some long-term consequences might be? Do the long-term consequences fit in with how you want your future to be?

My life at school now:

My actions	Short-term consequences	Possible long-term consequences	How will these affect my future?

1.5 My Quality World

Think about the people and things in your life that are important to you. Write or draw them on the 'My Quality World' sheet below.

Now add the people or things that you would like in your future world.

You have put together your **quality world** which contains all the things you need to make you happy.

Now look again. **Have you included your education?** If you haven't, is it because you forgot or don't you think it should be there? Discuss this point with your tutor.

If you have decided to include your education in your quality world, explain why it is there.

Section 2 Changing Behaviour

There are two sets of worksheets in this section. The first set helps pupils to understand the concept of 'behaviour' and the second set deals with changing behaviour.

Notes for Pupil Worksheets
(You may need to scribe for the pupil)

Behave! Behave! Behave! To many problem pupils, 'behaviour' often simply means, "the things I do wrong". This worksheet gets the students thinking about a definition of behaviour.

The Behaviour Picture sets out to widen the concept. Behaviour is actually four things. Of course it includes actions and the way in which those actions are performed, but it's more than this. *Thoughts* and *feelings* are the essential controlling force behind *actions* and *body language*. So the total behaviour picture needs to include not only the things that can be observed from the outside – actions and body language, but also what is going on inside an individual – their thoughts and feelings.

My Behaviour Picture and **Example of a Behaviour Picture** both reinforce the idea of the 'behaviour picture'. Then **Thoughts** takes this a step further. It gets pupils to understand the power of their thoughts in determining the way they feel and act. From here, it's only a small step to recognising that changing the way we think about situations can actually change the way in which we choose to act.

Two Worlds begins with a reminder of the earlier worksheet 'My Quality World' and then asks the pupil to investigate how much of this quality world overlaps with the real world in which he/she lives. Clearly the greater the overlap between the two the more satisfying life is. This is why it is so important that education is in the pupil's quality world.

Back to Behaviour guides students towards an understanding that getting a greater overlap, between their quality world and their real world, is within their own control – it's just a matter of changing their behaviour picture. At this point, it is important to reinforce the idea that, whilst others can influence our behaviour, they cannot change it. Each individual is ultimately in charge of and responsible for his or her own behaviour.

School: Whilst their education is probably part of their 'quality world', education comes as part of a package. That package is school. Some of the things in school may already be in the pupil's quality world, but other aspects may be problematic.

'School' gets the student to think about and then list both the good and bad aspects of school. It helps to identify things that need to be changed to make school more a part of the student's quality world. Trying to get too many changes at once is not a good idea.

Section 2: Changing Behaviour

Making a Change encourages the student to choose just one thing to change, while **Plan and Check** provides a way of planning the change and of reflecting back on the plan's effectiveness.

Small Changes – Big Differences will help to put the concept of change into perspective. The pupil is not being asked to become a different person, merely to make some small changes that will enhance the quality of life at school.

The final three worksheets provide ways of monitoring and maintaining changes. **The Captain's Log** and **The Captain's Chart** follow through the image of the boat on the 'Small Changes – Big Differences' worksheet. The idea is to encourage the students to feel in charge and think of themselves as steering their boat to a 'quality world'.

The worksheet **Instructions for using The Captain's Chart** needs to be discussed with the pupil before using the chart.

2.1 Behave! Behave! Behave!

Now let's think about behaviour. You hear about it all the time. Parents, teachers – they're always on about behaviour. This is the sort of thing you probably hear:

Perhaps you've even said this to yourself:

So what exactly is 'behaviour'? Discuss the word first with your tutor and then explain it below.

I think that behaviour is _____

_____

_____

_____

_____

It includes _____

_____

_____

_____

2.2 The Behaviour Picture

We usually think of behaviour as what someone does or says (actions). It's quite likely that this is what you thought about when you were explaining behaviour in the last worksheet.

But behaviour is actually more complicated than this. As well as **actions**, behaviour also includes **thoughts**, **feelings** and **body language**. This whole way of looking at behaviour is called the **behaviour picture**.

Look carefully at the behaviour picture below. When you think you understand, explain it to your tutor.

2.3 My Behaviour Picture

Now think about a problem situation in which you have been involved at school. First explain the situation and then construct your own behaviour picture for it.

The situation: (What happened)

My Behaviour Picture

My actions
What I did and said.

My thoughts
What I told myself.

My feelings

My body language

2.4 Example of a Behaviour Picture

Remember your behaviour picture is:

❖ what you do and say (actions)

❖ what you tell yourself (thoughts)

❖ your feelings

❖ your body language.

Now take a look at this situation.

> Andy and Mike are in a maths lesson. They're bored. Mike throws a pencil at Andy who laughs and throws it back. The teacher spots that Andy is messing around and not paying attention.
>
> She says sharply,
>
> "Behave yourself, Andy. Get on with your work."
>
> Andy angrily replies, "Tell Mike. He started it. Why do you always pick on me?"

What is Andy's behaviour picture? You'll have to guess his thoughts, feelings and body language.

Actions What Andy did and said	Thoughts What Andy told himself	Feelings How Andy felt	Body Language How Andy looked

2.5 Thoughts

You may have noticed that Andy could have changed what he did. He could have ignored Mike. He could have kept quiet when his teacher told him off. So why didn't he? **The answer is in Andy's head – his thoughts.** Here's what he was probably telling himself:

Here's how Andy's **actions** were controlled by his **thoughts**:

I'm bored. → Ready for some distractions

Let's have a bit of fun. → Throws the pencil back

Why me? Mike started it. Teachers always pick on me. → Speaks angrily to the teacher

Here's how Andy's **feelings** and **body language** were controlled by his **thoughts**:

Teachers always pick on me. → angry, clenched fists

So now you can see how powerful thoughts can be. Remember:

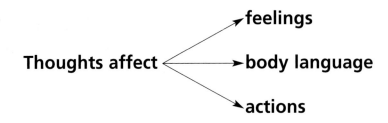

2.6 Two Worlds

Remember your **quality world**? That world which contains all of the things that are important to you and that you need and want in your life. Well, there is also another world. This is your **real world** – the one that exists around you and of which you are a part.

Hopefully, lots of the things that you wrote about or drew in your quality world are also in your real world. Or if they are not there yet, you can see that if things go how you plan, they may be there in the future.

Let's explore both your quality world and your real world and see how well they fit together. In the centre space below, describe the things that are in **both** of your worlds. In the ovals at the bottom, describe the things that exist only in one of your worlds.

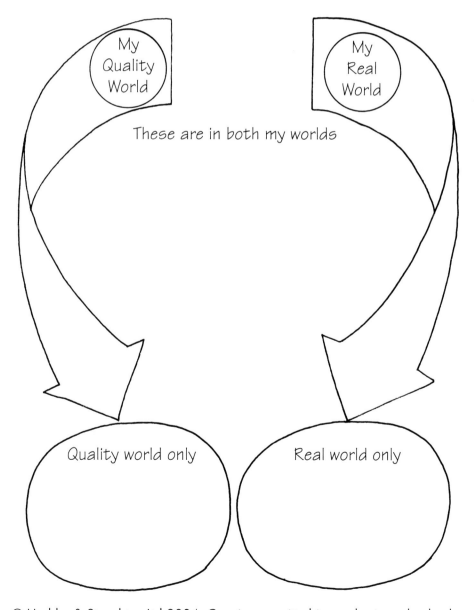

2.7 Back to Behaviour

Differences between a quality world and the real world often lead to strong negative feelings, like anger, irritation, sadness or fear. These feelings affect what you do, what you say and your body language. In fact, they affect your whole behaviour picture.

This is how your behaviour picture looks when your quality world and the real world are different.

Behaviour Picture	
Thoughts *I don't like this. It's not right for me. I'm not happy. I'm going to have to make some changes here.*	**Feelings** Irritated? Angry? Sad? Frightened? Worried? Bored?
Body language Tense muscles? Clenched fists? Frowning? Crying?	**Actions** I try to change things, to make them more as I would like them to be.

It's very important to recognise when there are big differences between your quality world and your real world. If this is the situation, then it's essential to work out ways of getting the worlds to overlap more. If you can do this successfully, you will be happier.

But this is where a lot of people go wrong. They often start by trying to get others to change. This can be a hard task and, in fact, it's actually impossible unless those other people choose to change.

So, if you want changes, the best place to start is with yourself, with your own behaviour picture.

If you choose your behaviour wisely, there is every chance that you will be happier. It's also possible that changing your behaviour will influence other people to change theirs in ways that are helpful to you.

Talk this through with your tutor, before moving on to the next worksheet.

2.8 School

School is obviously part of your real world and it's likely that you consider your own education to be part of your quality world. But as well as your education, school includes rules, lessons, teachers, other pupils, break time, lunch time and so on. If you want an education, you can't escape all the other things that go along with school.

Even if you are not overfond of school as a whole, there are probably some bits that *do* make you happy. You might be pleased to see your friends there each day. Break or lunch times might give you a chance to play football or have a chat. Some lessons you might find interesting or fun. Some teachers you might get on with OK. So parts of school are probably in your quality world. Other things about school will not be part of your quality world. If these are making you unhappy then they need sorting out.

On one side of the grid below, write down the people or things at school that are in your quality world. Then fill in the things that cause you problems and make you unhappy.

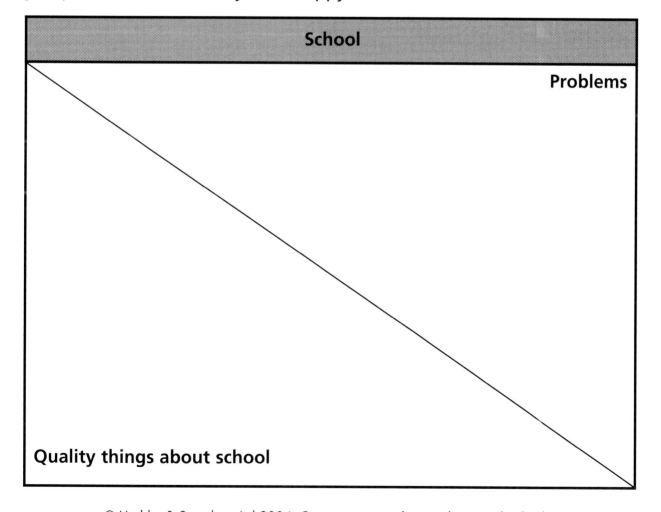

© Hodder & Stoughton Ltd 2004. Copying permitted in purchasing school only.

2.9 Making a Change

❖ Look again at the problems on the last worksheet about school. Which one would you most like to sort out?

_____
_____
_____
_____

❖ Next, think of one thing **you** can do over the next week to lessen the problem. This must be something that you can do yourself. It must not depend on anyone else doing something.

Write down what you could do:

_____
_____
_____
_____
_____
_____

❖ Are you really willing to give this a try over the coming week?

❖ Discuss this with your tutor.

❖ If you are willing to give it a go, use the next worksheet, Plan and Check, to help you.

2.10 Plan and Check

The Plan: Before you start your behaviour change, fill in **Grid A**.

Grid A
The present situation:
Here's the behaviour change I'm going to try out:
This is how I'm hoping things will improve:
I think that it will be useful to let these people know what I'm planning to do:

Check Back: Fill in **Grid B** when you have tried out your change for a week.

Grid B
Did the change improve things for me? If it did, how?
Was anyone else's behaviour influenced by my change? How?
Should I keep going with this change?
Should I try another change? What?

2.11 Small Changes – Big Differences

Look at this boat. Can you see that a small change in direction can make a big difference to where the boat ends up?

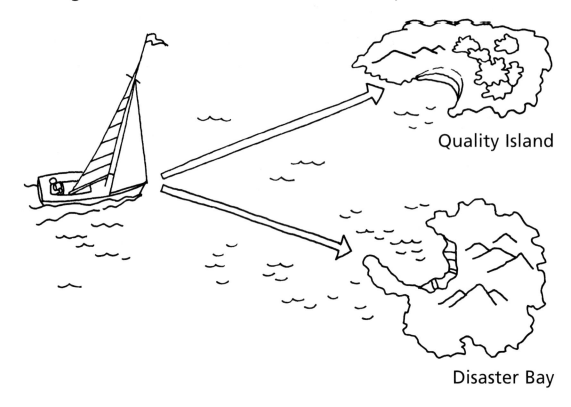

Quality Island

Disaster Bay

It's just the same for you. Making some small changes to your behaviour can make big differences to the quality of your life.

You've made a start with one change. Later, you may want to make some adjustments or add some more changes.

Don't try to change by yourself. Arrange to meet regularly with your tutor to discuss how things are working out and to decide on further changes.

Remember, just like the captain of a boat, you're in charge of any changes that you make. The next two worksheets will help you to set your course and steer in the right direction.

2.12 The Captain's Log

Use this log to decide on the changes that you need to make. When you have decided on a change, write it in the first column. Then discuss with your tutor **how** you are actually going to do it and **when** you intend to start. The last three columns are so that you and your tutor can check your progress. Remember, regular check-ups will help you to make your changes permanent.

Changes	Maintenance Checks		
What? How? When?	Date Report	Date Report	Date Report

2.13 Instructions for using The Captain's Chart

As well as using the Captain's Log, you might like to keep a record of your progress by using the next worksheet, The Captain's Chart. You plot your progress like you would on a graph. Here's an example.

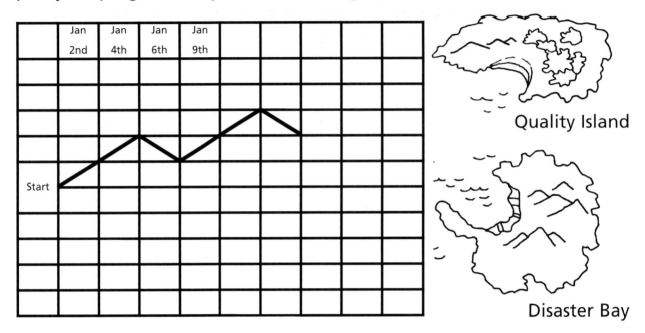

Quality Island

Disaster Bay

Before you start to use the chart, here are some things you need to think about:

❖ Would a lesson monitor help you to keep a check on your progress? Your tutor could give you one from the general worksheets called 'Helping _____ to be a winner'. Have a look at it and see if you think it's suitable. Alternatively, you might decide to construct a personal monitor or use one that is in general use in your school.

❖ How often are you going to record your progress on the chart? Every day? Every few days? Once a week?

❖ Who is going to help you to fill in the chart? Your tutor? Another support teacher? Your form teacher? Your year head?

❖ How often are you going to discuss your progress with your tutor?

❖ Who is going to look after the chart?

❖ If you make good progress, how are you going to make sure that other people recognise the efforts you have been making? Phone-call, postcard, letter home? Newsflash? Certificate?

Discuss these points and any others that you can think of with your tutor.

2.14 The Captain's Chart

Write down the things you want for your future on Quality Island and your problems in Disaster Bay. Now chart your changes and see where you are heading.

Date	Date	Date	Date	Date	Date	Date	Date	Date	Date

Quality Island

(chart grid)

Start

Disaster Bay

Section 3 Back-up Skills

This concluding set of worksheets offers some additional skills, which will be useful to pupils who have made a decision to change their behaviour.

Notes for Pupil Worksheets
(You may need to scribe for the pupil)

Get Sensitive to Situations, Build Up and **Spotting the Critical Moments**. Situations don't just happen. They occur as part of a wider picture. These first three worksheets alert students to the way in which problems arise and develop. This is about developing awareness not just to situations but how the pupil could react in those situations. It is about choice and tutors need to reinforce the concept that the student can and does choose the way he/she thinks about situations. The tutor then needs to re-emphasise that thoughts influence the way we feel and act.

Danger – Keep Clear! helps pupils to utilise their self-awareness to avoid running into difficulties in lessons. Your own knowledge of the pupil should be used if he/she is unaware of likely pitfalls.

Trying or Doing? focuses on making the student understand that if change is to occur, then commitment needs to be total. It's insufficient to say, "I'll try" because that already contains the message that it might not work.

Take Up Modelling asks the pupil to think about how other people deal with problem situations and to consider if these methods might work for him or her.

3.1 Get Sensitive to Situations

At school you are faced with lots of different situations. Some work out well for you. In other situations, you need to tread very carefully. The next few worksheets will teach you how to weigh up situations so you can steer yourself away from trouble. Here are two situations, both involving the same boy, Rakesh. Read them both carefully. For each one think about what was happening **around** Rakesh.

Situation A

As Rakesh goes into class, he sees his English teacher, Mrs Potter. He knows that life can be tough if you fall out with Mrs Potter. The room is quiet. Most people are in their places and ready to start the lesson. Rakesh goes over to his usual place, sits down and waits for Mrs Potter to begin. He works hard for the next hour.

Situation B

As Rakesh goes into the class, someone shouts "Potter's away". Rakesh hears a lot of chatter and notices that people are not in their usual seats. In fact lots of people are not even in a seat, but wandering about the room. Rakesh decides to sit next to Tom. 'Tom's always a good laugh,' he thinks. After a few minutes, the teacher turns up and then it takes a bit more time to sort out the work. The class is still noisy. Several people are calling to others across the classroom. Then a rubber whizzes through the air and catches Rakesh sharply on the ear. "Ouch!" he shouts and chucks it back in the direction it came from. The teacher orders Rakesh out of the room. As he leaves the room, the head teacher appears outside the classroom.

We call what was going on around Rakesh 'the **background** to the situation'. The background to each situation has some things that are similar and some that are different. Some things in the background certainly influenced the way Rakesh thought about each situation.

What influenced his thoughts in Situation A? _____

_____

_____

What influenced his thoughts in Situation B? _____

_____

_____

3.2 Build Up

We know that actions don't just happen by themselves; they are part of a whole behaviour picture. You have already decided the ways in which the background to each situation had some influence on Rakesh. But to understand why Rakesh actually acted in the way he did, we also need to look at other things. One of these is how each situation **builds up**.

On the grid below, the background information for **Situation A** has been written in. Can you complete Rakesh's behaviour picture and show how the situation built up for him. You will have to guess some of his thoughts, feelings and body language.

Situation A – The Build Up

Background	Rakesh's Behaviour Picture			
	Thoughts	Feelings	Body language	Actions
Rakesh sees Mrs Potter.				
The room is quiet.				
People are in their places ready to start.				

Situation B: Now draw a larger grid and complete it using the following background facts: 1. Someone shouts "Potter's away". 2. Lots of chatter, people in different seats or wandering around. 3. Teacher's late, takes time to sort out work. 4. Class is noisy, people are shouting across the classroom. 5. A rubber hits Rakesh. 6. Rakesh is ordered out of the room. 7. The head teacher is outside the classroom.

3.3 Spotting the Critical Moments

As well as being able to see the build up in situations, it's also important to be able to spot **critical moments**. A 'critical moment' is the point in a situation where someone actually does something. In other words, it's the moment when they take action. Here's an example from Situation A on worksheet 3.1.

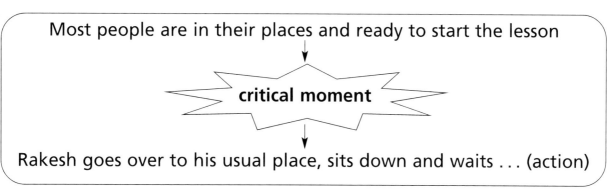

Here's another example from Situation B.

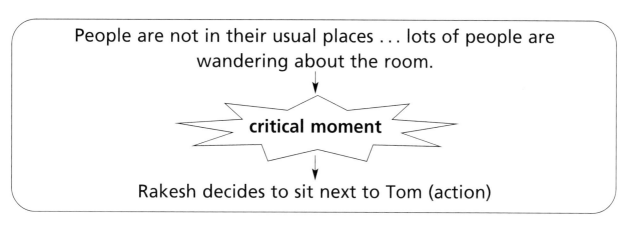

Look again at Situation B. Find another critical moment and write it in the box below.

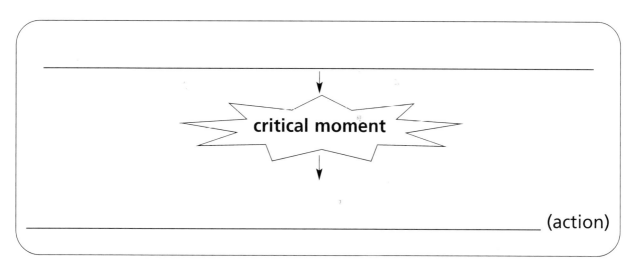

3.4 Danger – Keep Clear!

You probably started this unit because you have been running into trouble in class. Possibly, in some lessons you get along fine, but in others it might be just like walking into a field full of unexploded bombs.

In these situations, you need to:

❖ be very watchful;

❖ be aware of problems building up;

❖ act carefully; and

❖ think of the consequences.

Think of one particular lesson in which you often have problems. Then, use the grid below to plan how you'll handle this in future.

The things I need to watch out for at the start of this lesson.	
Ways that problems sometimes build up and how I can avoid getting involved.	

Try out your ideas and report back to your tutor. If they work, stick with them and develop more ideas for other lessons. If they don't work, revise your plans and try again.

3.5 Trying or Doing?

Spot the difference:

"I'll **try** to put my hand up instead of shouting out."

"I'll put my hand up instead of shouting out."

"I'll try to put my hand up instead of shouting out"

means: _____

_____

_____

"I'll put my hand up instead of shouting out"

means: _____

_____

_____

When you decide on a change:

Do it. Don't just try!

3.6 Take Up Modelling

What's a **role model**? Discuss this with your tutor and then write your own definition below.

> A role model is:

Now explain the difference between a **good** role model and a **bad** role model.

Lots of famous people are role models. Think of a well-known person who you would choose as a good role model. Describe your role model and how he or she influences your behaviour. (Remember behaviour is thoughts, feelings, actions and body language.)

Role models don't have to be famous. There are people in your year group who manage to be interesting and fun, but don't get into lots of bother in class. They get the balance right between enjoying themselves and getting on OK in school, so they're worth observing.

Choose someone in your class who could be a good role model for you. Over the next week watch how he or she deals with different situations. Think about whether you can learn from how they handle problems.

At the end of the week, discuss your findings with your tutor.

Unit 2
Conflict Resolution

Tutor Notes – Introduction

We usually regard conflict as something bad. It evokes thoughts of wars, fights, arguments, winners or losers and is less often looked upon as an opportunity to resolve differences, to find common areas of agreement or to move on in a relationship. In fact conflict in itself is neither positive nor negative, merely an inevitable part of life, which arises because individuals, groups or nations have divergent needs or desires. It is the reaction to conflict which makes it either a destructive force or an opportunity for constructive dialogue and growth. *Conflict Resolution* focuses on helping pupils to understand the nature of a conflict and manage it so it has beneficial outcomes for all involved. Essentially, it is a problem-solving exercise.

Structure of the Course

The course is in three sections. The first, **About Conflict Resolution** ensures that pupils understand the nature of conflict and are able to evaluate the various ways in which it can be resolved. Section 2, **Everyone's a Winner** takes students through the stages of negotiating a settlement acceptable to everyone, and the final part, **Skills for Conflict Resolution** concentrates on various personal skills which could be useful in achieving a satisfactory resolution to conflict.

The Nature of Conflict

Conflict is about satisfying needs. These can be about actual physical requirements such as access to fresh water to drink, land to grow food, or raw materials for housing, manufacturing and commerce. They can also include wants, for example more money, improved living conditions or more time to do things. But, material needs are not the whole story. In addition to these, we all have powerful psychological requirements. Everyone, in some way, has a need to belong to others. Being accepted as a member of a family or as part of a particular social grouping is vitally important to our sense of well-being. Being excluded makes us feel uncomfortable or unhappy and often results in conflict. Other psychological needs such as freedom and independence, the power to make our own choices in life, achieving recognition and respect from others, a sense of fun and enjoyment are equally important basic needs and, consequently, they are potential sources of conflict.

Value Systems

Conflicts are often more difficult to resolve because the main adversaries have differing values, beliefs or priorities. An adolescent falling out with his/her parents is an obvious example of this. Whilst the need to belong to a peer group might be the teenager's main concern, Mum or Dad may be more interested in their offspring's educational attainment or how they function within the family grouping.

Where differing value systems are involved, an important first step in resolving conflict is to acknowledge other people's positions. If each party recognises where others are coming from they will be less likely to reject each other outright. As a result they will be more able to concentrate on the main areas of disagreement and develop solutions acceptable to all.

Responding to Conflict

When a conflict arises, there are three basic ways that adversaries can respond to the situation. They can give in, try to force the opposition to back down or negotiate a settlement. We have named

these the **soft, tough** and **smart** approaches. 'Soft' and 'tough' often bring about one-sided solutions to conflict – one side wins because the other either concedes or loses in a dispute. Thus both are unsatisfactory and will typically result in bad feeling between the participants. The 'smart' approach is the only one that can meet the needs of everyone and help to maintain good relationships in the future.

Soft Responses

Soft responses can occur in a number of ways – by avoiding issues, by simply accommodating to someone else's needs or by agreeing to a compromise that is not really in anyone's interests. Sometimes friends who want to maintain good relationships will steer clear of an open conflict by ignoring it or denying it matters. Alternatively, disputes are sometimes resolved by doing something that neither party wants – Jack wants to go to the cinema, Jane wants to visit friends, and so they end up staying in. This is a **lose–lose** situation, because no one ends up getting what they want. 'Soft' responses can also result in **lose–win** situations when one party gives in without making clear his/her own needs in the situation. For instance, one person might get his or her own way time after time, but eventually this may well lead to the breakdown of the relationship or friendship. So, ultimately, 'soft' reactions are unsatisfactory because they leave at least one person's needs unmet and thus they typically lead to feelings of frustration, apprehension, disappointment or concern about the future.

Tough Responses

Tough responses are characterised by a desire to make others back down. People who take a tough stand want victory and are often willing to belittle, argue, threaten, punish or use force if necessary to achieve their ends. There is no room for compromise; they are after a **win–lose** result. However, sometimes this approach backfires, the tough individual does not get what he or she wants and neither does his or her adversary. For instance, a bully might hope to consolidate his/her power position within a group by picking on a weaker member. The latter may be forced to back down and thus lose. But other group members may become wary of the bully and also back away from him/her and so he/she loses the thing they really wanted – status within the group. Thus a **lose–lose** situation results.

Smart Responses

The smart response is a problem-solving exercise. Those involved don't want the victory or submission of any of the participants, they simply want a solution that is in the best interests of everyone. To do this they are willing to co-operate, listen to others, focus on needs rather than personalities and draw up an agreement that ensures the welfare of everyone. This is the only response that can give a **win–win** outcome.

Section 4 About Conflict Resolution

This section has two major objectives. First of all, it aims to give students a basic understanding of the nature of conflict. Then it presents them with opportunities to explore their own conflict situations and consider how they generally try to resolve them.

Notes for Pupil Worksheets
(You may need to scribe for the pupil)

Conflict Resolution – What is it? For this worksheet it would be useful to have a dictionary and a thesaurus handy. This will enable the student to investigate the terms 'conflict' and 'resolution' for themselves.

Needs and **Needs and Conflict** look at the causes of conflict and focus particularly on the sort of psychological needs that create conflicts in school. **Exploring My Own Conflicts** follows on from this and helps students to gain an insight into their own conflicts and identify unmet needs.

Soft, Tough or Smart introduces the three strategies for dealing with conflict – give way, confront or negotiate. It then asks the student to identify his or her own preferred style of conflict resolution. **Win or Lose?** helps the pupils to evaluate the success of each of the three approaches and hopefully leads them to identify the smart approach as the way to successful conflict resolution.

4.1 Conflict Resolution – What is it?

The word **conflict** has a number of meanings. Here are some of them:

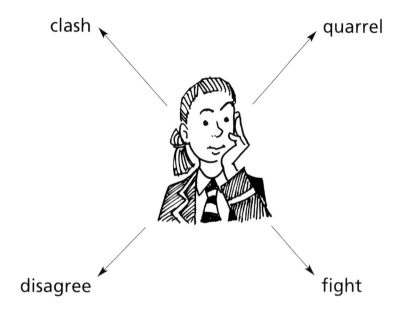

clash   quarrel   disagree   fight

Use a dictionary or thesaurus to find some other words for conflict and write them below.

_____   _____   _____   _____

The word **resolution** also has a number of meanings. Here are some of them:

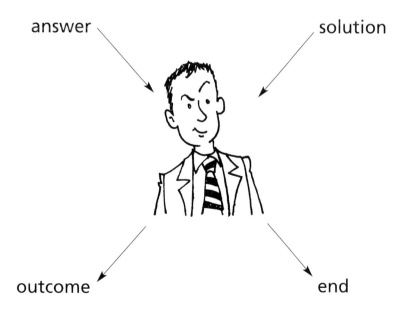

answer   solution   outcome   end

So, **conflict resolution** means _____

_____

4.2 Needs

We all **need** a variety of things to keep us **healthy** and **happy**.

On the picture below, list some of the things that we need to keep our bodies **healthy**.

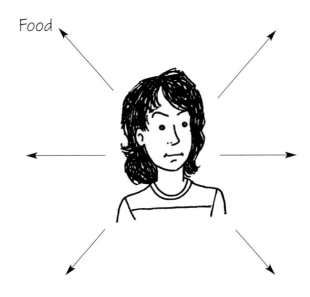

Now think about the things that we need to keep us **happy**.

List some of them below.

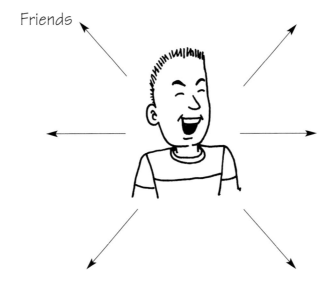

4.3 Needs and Conflict

Conflicts happen when people haven't got the things they need. Most of us are lucky enough to have the things that we need to keep our bodies healthy, so we don't tend to get into conflicts over basic needs like food or drink.

Conflicts in school generally happen because people feel dissatisfied in other ways. Here are some common complaints:

They decide everything.	I've got no **power**.
They won't let me join in.	I never seem to **belong**.
He always stops me doing things.	I have no **freedom**.
She's rude to me.	I never get **respect**.
They're spoil-sports.	I never get any **fun**.

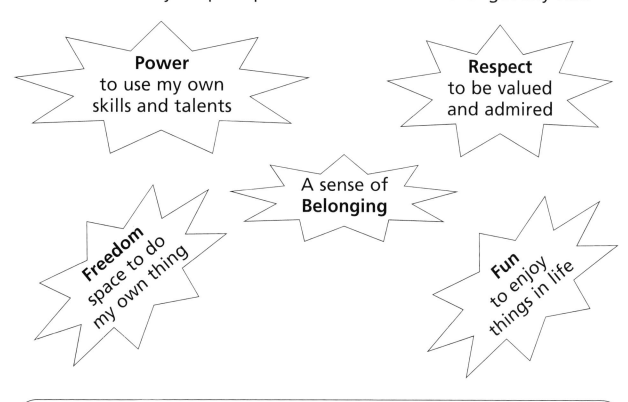

- **Power** to use my own skills and talents
- **Respect** to be valued and admired
- A sense of **Belonging**
- **Freedom** space to do my own thing
- **Fun** to enjoy things in life

> **Power, Belonging, Respect, Freedom, Fun**
>
> are important to everyone.

4.4 Exploring My Own Conflicts

❖ What sort of conflicts do you get involved in?

❖ Who do you tend to disagree or argue with?

❖ Which of your needs do you feel are sometimes not being satisfied?

    Power?   Belonging?   Respect?   Freedom?   Fun?

Fill in the grid below. This will help you to investigate the ways in which conflict is part of your life.

The Conflict	Who was involved?	What need was I trying to satisfy?

4.5 Soft, Tough or Smart

You can deal with conflicts in three basic ways.

❖ You can give in, ignore what has happened, or hope it will go away. This is a **soft** way of sorting things out.

❖ You can argue, threaten, say something hurtful, shout, push or hit out. This is a **tough** way of dealing with conflicts.

❖ You can try to settle things so everyone feels reasonably satisfied. This involves listening, trying to understand different points of view and showing respect for others. This is a **smart** way of settling disagreements.

So, what's your style – soft, tough or smart? Fill in the grid below. It will help you to understand how you usually settle conflicts.

Conflict	What I did	My Style

4.6 Win or Lose?

Different ways of dealing with conflict will give different results.

❖ Who is likely to be the winner from a **soft** response?

❖ Who is likely to be the winner from a **tough** response?

❖ Who is likely to be the winner from a **smart** response?

Consider the risks of each approach by filling in the grid below.

Style	What's the risk?	What's the gain?	Who probably wins?
Soft (ignore, avoid, withdraw etc.)			
Tough (threaten, hit, shout, push etc.)			
Smart (explain, listen, work together, look for solutions etc.)			

Which method always guarantees a win?

Section 5 Everyone's a Winner

The 'smart' approach is not just about asking pupils to "Be nice to each other" or telling them simply to "Talk it through". It's much more than this. It's about teaching a very definite set of procedures for achieving sustainable resolutions to conflict. It provides a process in which all participants can feel satisfied that their needs are being addressed and, if successful, will not only end hostilities but can also actually strengthen relationships.

Notes for Pupil Worksheets
(You may need to scribe for the pupil)

The Smart Approach sets out an overview of this approach. It is useful for tutors to look carefully at this so they have a good general idea of what is involved.

Agree to Negotiate introduces pupils to the concept of negotiation as well as exploring any of their own successful negotiations.

Using a Mediator explains the mediator's role in the negotiation process. At this point it would be interesting to also explore the rights of each of the participants and lay down a set of rules for how discussion should take place.

Gather Points of View and **Focus on Needs** help the participants to identify their own thoughts, feelings and needs. The idea is to let pupils fill these in individually, so that they can act as notes when they are putting over their own positions and viewpoints in any ensuing discussions.

Making Plans and **Weigh Up Your Plans**. Once everyone has had an opportunity to clearly state his/her own position and understood the thoughts, feelings and needs of others involved, the negotiation needs to move on. These worksheets guide the participants through this stage.

Our Agreement is the final step, drawing up a written agreement that is acceptable to all. Make sure that everyone has a copy of this.

5.1 The Smart Approach

Step 1: Agree to negotiate

Accept that you have a problem that needs sorting out.

Step 2: Agree on a mediator

Choose a person who will not take sides and will help everyone to focus on finding solutions.

Step 3: Gather points of view

Recognise that other people have their own opinions. Respect their right to have these opinions, even if you disagree with them. Explain your position and be prepared to listen to others.

Step 4: Focus on needs

What's causing the problem? Not belonging? No space? Lack of respect? No fun? No power?

Step 5: Look for win–win solutions

Draw up some plans. Make sure there are gains for everyone.

Step 6: Weigh up your plans

Find the one that gives the most gains to everyone.

Step 7: Set up your agreement

Make sure everyone is clear about the agreement and their part in making it work.

5.2 Agree to Negotiate

When you negotiate:

❖ you make an effort to talk things through in a calm way;

❖ you try to think your way around any difficulties and obstacles; and

❖ you try to find a win–win solution. That is a solution that satisfies everyone involved.

Have you ever been involved in a successful negotiation where you sorted out problems by discussing them? If you have, use the box below to explain what happened.

Who was involved?	
What was the problem?	
What was the solution?	
Was it a win–win solution?	

When you negotiate, you should:

Keep calm   *Be ready to listen*

Look for common ground   *Respect the views of others*

Be willing to move on

5.3 Using a Mediator

A mediator's job is a bit like being a referee or an umpire. He or she never takes sides, but tries to understand everyone's point of view. Mediators help adversaries to find good solutions to their conflict.

The mediator starts by setting the 'ground rules' for discussion. What do you think should be included in these rules? Complete the grid below to show your ideas.

Rule	Reason
Everyone involved should speak calmly.	People will only listen and think about things if they are spoken to in a reasonable manner.
Everyone should have an equal chance to speak.	

Once everyone has had a chance to say how they feel about the situation, the mediator then asks for some possible solutions to the conflict.

When a solution has been agreed, the mediator makes sure that everyone clearly understands the agreement. Sometimes this is written down and everyone concerned is given a copy.

5.4 Gather Points of View

Whatever the conflict, it is important to recognise that everyone will have a viewpoint.

Obviously, it's essential that you are able to explain your own position well. Use the grid below to prepare yourself for this. It uses 'I' statements to help you concentrate on putting over your own thoughts and feelings about the situation instead of just blaming others.

I feel _____   _____
The reason I feel _____ is because _____   _____
I would like _____   _____   _____
I understand that you feel _____ because _____   _____
I think that a good solution to our conflict would be _____   _____

5.5 Focus on Needs

Remember!

Conflicts happen when people haven't got the things they need.

So conflicts can only be resolved if everyone feels that their needs are being satisfied to some extent.

In your negotiations, this grid may be useful in exploring the needs of each person involved in the conflict.

Some of my thoughts on the situation _____

_____

_____

_____

_____

These lead me to feel _____

_____

_____

_____

_____

I feel _____ because my needs are not being satisfied in the following ways: _____

_____

_____

Power?   Belonging?   Respect?   Freedom?   Fun?

5.6 Making Plans

Now that each person has had a chance to explain his or her views and needs, the next step is to make plans to resolve the conflict. These must include some gains for everyone, so, as you might expect, there will also need to be some give and take.

Use the grid below to help you to explore possible ways that the conflict can be resolved.

Plan	For	Against
Plan A		
Plan B		
Plan C		

5.7 Weigh Up Your Plans

When a dispute is settled, people usually have to **compromise** (that is, to accept a bit less than they would really like). Look again at your plans and decide the advantages and disadvantages for each person involved in the conflict.

Name _____

Plan	Advantages	Disadvantages
A		
B		
C		

Name _____

Plan	Advantages	Disadvantages
A		
B		
C		

Name _____

Plan	Advantages	Disadvantages
A		
B		
C		

Our Agreement

Signed

Section 6 Skills for Conflict Resolution

If people go into negotiations in an angry mood or express themselves in confrontational ways, there is much less chance of a successful resolution to a conflict. The following worksheets give some thought to preparing students for the negotiation process.

Notes for Pupil Worksheets
(You may need to scribe for the pupil)

The Ups and Downs of Conflict illustrates how easy it is for anger to build up in a conflict situation and enables pupils to realise that what they say and how they say it matter. In his/her own eyes an angry person is right but in that angry state it is virtually impossible to think rationally. Thus the first step for angry participants is **Cooling Off Time**. Further details of calming procedures and a tutor worksheet on calming down an angry pupil can be found in *Anger Management*, Unit 3.

Learn to Listen. Good listening skills are essential for everyone involved in conflict resolution. It's a good idea to carry out some role-play to help the pupil really understand what is required. For further work on listening skills involving role-plays look at worksheet 14.2.

Prepare Yourself is a planning sheet for an actual negotiation in which the pupil is involved. A student/tutor role-play of the negotiation would considerably add to the effectiveness of the preparation.

The language we use in conflict situations can either inflame or calm down matters. **Explain, Don't Blame** and **'I' Not 'You'**, illustrate how changing from 'blaming' by using the word 'you' to 'explaining' by using the word 'I' can change the whole nature of an interaction.

Handle Criticism. An inability to handle valid criticism demonstrates a basic lack of confidence. The truly confident person can accept valid criticism but reject criticism with which he/she does not agree. This worksheet puts forward an assertive strategy for dealing with criticism coupled with an appropriate use of language.

Don't Obstruct complements the earlier worksheet on listening skills. It is basically explaining the normal rules of conversation where you respect the rights of others.

Notes for Tutor Worksheet

Empathy (Understanding Others). Psychotherapists in relationship counselling commonly use this technique. This will make the pupil really think about how another person in a conflict situation is feeling. It will also help him/her to understand how outsiders view the conflict.

6.1 The Ups and Downs of Conflict

Just like escalators, conflicts can go up and down. When a conflict gets bigger and more intense, we say it **escalates** and when it goes down, we say it **de-escalates**.

Look at this situation and watch how it escalates:

	Alan	Pete
Rudeness	"Move! I sit there."	"Hard luck. You're too late!"
Name calling, threats	"I said 'move', you slug."	"Call me that again and I'll smash your face in."
Fighting	"Just try!" (Alan pushes Pete)	"Take that, you jerk." (Pete punches Alan)

It escalated because neither Alan nor Pete really attempted to avoid a conflict. They both just reacted to the situation and to each other. Neither took charge and tried to calm things down.

Think about the start of this situation again.

Alan is annoyed because Pete is sitting where Alan usually sits. How could Alan express his feelings without allowing the situation to escalate?

_____

Pete is angry because Alan is rude to him. How could Pete make his feelings known and also de-escalate the situation?

_____

In life, conflict situations occur all the time. You probably can't avoid them, but you can learn to manage them.

6.2 Cooling Off Time

Conflicts can't always be resolved immediately. This is particularly true if people are very angry or tired. So sometimes it's better to put things on hold and allow everyone to get into the right mood for sorting out difficult problems. This is called a 'cooling off time'.

Cooling off time can be used for reflecting on the conflict. But remember, you are only seeing it from one side and if you think too much about things, you are in danger of working up your feelings and putting yourself into a bad temper.

The best way of cooling off is to do something that takes your mind off the conflict. You could perhaps:

Can you think of anything that would be a good cooling off activity for you?

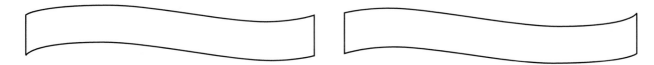

Remember: Cool off before you act!

6.3 Learn to Listen

Conflicts cannot be resolved unless people are willing to actively listen to each other. This means really concentrating and trying to understand what is being said. You need to show the speaker that you are actually doing this.

On the grid below there is a list of behaviours that make for active listening. Can you work out why each one is important?

Behaviour	Why is it important?
Sit in a relaxed way.	
Don't fidget.	
Look at the speaker.	
Nod if you agree with something.	
Don't interrupt, wait for a pause before speaking.	
When there is a suitable pause, ask for things you don't understand to be explained.	
Before you explain your own position, summarise what has been said so far.	

6.4 Prepare Yourself

Discussions where people are talking about their feelings can be difficult, so it's often best to make some preparations. If you know in advance what you are going to say, you are likely to explain yourself in a clearer and more confident way. Also, if you have thought about how you and others may feel during the conversation, you will be able to work out a plan for dealing with strong emotions. For instance, if you know that the discussion might make you tense and angry, you might decide to deal with this by using some relaxation techniques before you start. Use the grid below to help you to think things through.

	Possible ideas	**How I have decided to deal with this**
How do you think you will feel?		
How do you think other people will feel?		
What will you say?		
What do you think other people will say?		
Are there any other things that concern you?		

6.5 Explain, Don't Blame

When someone does something you don't like, it's easy just to heap blame on them.

> You pig! You messed up the room and left me to clear everything up. You do that again and I'll tip your stuff out of the window.

Look again at the blame statement above. Have you noticed how many times the word 'you' is used?

In conflict situations, **'you' statements** often escalate disagreements. They blame ("You messed up the room"), they insult ("You pig"), they threaten ("You do that again and I'll…").

The opposite of 'you' statements are **'I' statements**. They explain feelings, concerns, views, wishes and so on.

> I felt really mad when I was left to clear up all that mess, especially as I didn't make any of it. Next time I expect you to clear up or I'll have to take some action.

Remember!
When you find yourself in a conflict situation, always try and use **'I' statements.** In this way you will get your views and feelings across without escalating things.

6.6 'I' Not 'You'

Look at the following 'you' messages. Can you change them into 'I' messages? Fill in your ideas in the boxes below.

You Message	I Message
You always make me come in early. You make me look such a fool in front of my friends. It will be your fault if I end up without any friends.	

You Message	I Message
You're really mean to me. You always clear off with Sarita and Emma. You forget that I have feelings. You always do whatever you want even if it means leaving me on my own.	

You Message	I Message
Get that jacket off, you know it's mine. You're always pinching my things without asking. You wear your own clothes in future.	

6.7 Handle Criticism

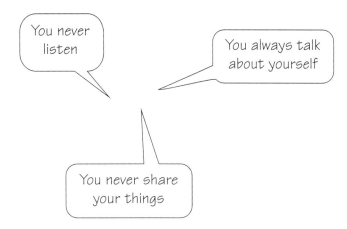

- No one likes being criticised. It hurts, makes us feel threatened and we sometimes deal with it by getting angry or saying something hurtful back.

- Hard responses like these often escalate into conflict, so it's important to develop other ways of dealing with criticism.

Here are some ideas to help you:

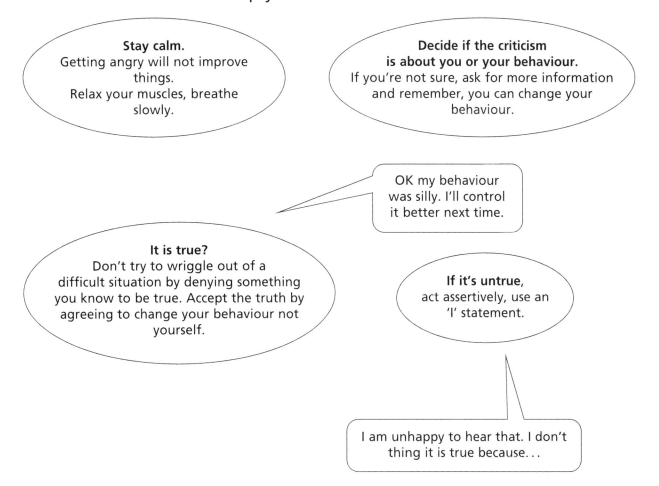

6.8 Don't Obstruct

Some attitudes and behaviours simply block useful discussions and conversations. They certainly won't help to resolve conflicts and they may actually intensify them. Here are some conversation blockers to avoid.

 It's really frustrating to be constantly interrupted. If it happens over and over again, people just give up trying to put over their viewpoint.

Advice can be positive if wanted, but unasked for advice can be annoying. People like to make their own decisions.

 Always talking about your own views, ideas and interests can be very boring to other people. If you dominate a discussion, other people will stop listening.

Don't try to control discussions. Demanding answers often makes others feel threatened. Share the discussion, but don't take it over.

 Negative and sarcastic comments are hurtful and lead to resentment. They have no place in good discussions.

6.9 Tutor Worksheet:
Empathy (Understanding Others)

Note: *Read through this sheet carefully before trying it with your student. Then arrange 4 chairs like this.*

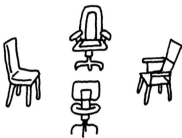

This is a script, read the instructions carefully to the pupil, pausing for replies where appropriate.

❖ Sit on chair 1

    Think about the person with whom you are in conflict.
        What makes your relationship difficult?
        Is it to do with the way you behave?
        Is it to do with your skills or abilities at something?
        Is it about the ideas you have?
        Is it about who you are?
        Anything else?

❖ Sit on chair 2

    Now imagine that you're not yourself, but you're the person with whom you are in conflict. That person is thinking about you.
        Describe your thoughts.
        Describe your feelings.
        Describe your concerns.

❖ Sit on chair 3

    You are now an outsider. You are thinking about the relationship between the two people in front of you. In chair 1 see yourself and in chair 2 see the person you find difficult to get on with.
        What sort of relationship is this?
        What do you think about these two people?
        How do you feel about their relationship?
        Can you see any need for change? What? Why? How?

❖ Sit on chair 4

    You are now wiser. Be yourself again.
        Look at yourself in chair 1 – do you want to change anything?
        Look at the other person in chair 2 – do you understand any of their thoughts, feelings, and concerns?
        Do you want to make any changes in your relationship? How?

Unit 3
Anger Management

Tutor Notes – Introduction

You know what anger is. You will have experienced it. You will have at sometime been the recipient of it. But before using the worksheets in this section, take a little time to consider the notes below. They will help you to understand the *nature* of anger and where it comes from. This knowledge, plus an appreciation of why particular activities and techniques have been chosen in this anger management course, will, we hope, strengthen the sessions you have with your students.

Anger almost certainly developed as a survival strategy in response to pain or threat. However, underlying the whole philosophy of this unit is that anger is not an appropriate response in everyday life at home, at school, at work or at play. This concept needs to be reinforced again and again.

Structure of the Course

The first section **Dealing with an Angry Child** is about coping with the immediate consequences of anger. The two worksheets in this section could be of use for in-service training. The next section **Assessing the Anger** is essentially the starting point of an anger management programme with students. It provides a diagnostic tool that will help the tutor to assess the reasons for the student's anger outbursts. It will also guide the tutor in the selection of optional worksheets in Section 12. The **Basic Anger Management Programme** is in Sections 9, 10 and 11 and we suggest that all students should complete this. The programme covers a range of techniques for calming down. It also teaches the pupil how to think differently so that anger does not build up and encourages him/her to behave in an assertive way. Finally the **Additional Worksheets** in Section 12 may be useful for the specific problems of certain students. Attention-seeking behaviour, accepting responsibility for one's actions and learning how to handle criticism are addressed in this section.

Understanding Anger

Anger is a behaviour that can be learnt
If a child learns to get his or her way by throwing a tantrum, more tantrums are sure to follow. Similarly, if an older child or an adult finds that anger forces other people to back down, this strategy will be reinforced. Anger is not a healthy release of energy and emotions; it is a behavioural strategy to achieve an end. Success simply means that it will be used again.

Anger can be addictive
An angry person, who gets their way, feels powerful and the accompanying changes in their body can be quite pleasurable. For this reason, the school bully who uses anger to build his or her power base gets gratification from the cowed responses of other children. Unless there is some intervention, it is highly likely that a child bully will grow up to be an adult bully. Teachers also often employ anger to control children's behaviour. How often have you seen seemingly insoluble conflict situations occur when angry child meets angry teacher?

Anger thresholds
Patterns of anger are learnt, but circumstances can lower a person's anger threshold. Pain, tiredness, hunger, alcohol and emotional problems at home or with friends are all examples of things that can make an angry response more likely. So in dealing with an angry child, it is important to understand any environmental factors that help to trigger angry episodes.

An angry person is always right

When anger comes on the scene, reason and logic go out of the window. The angry person is sure that he or she is right and the greater the intensity of anger, the greater the certainty of rightness. To understand this we need to consider the evolutionary origins of anger. Early man, living in a hostile and frightening environment, could not afford to be unsure of what to do when danger was around. He could not afford to stop and think when he was about to be attacked. It was a case of fight or run and the chosen response had to be instantaneous. An angry reaction to something originates in the same area of the brain as this 'fight/flight' response. It is immediate and when it occurs the thinking parts of the brain are by-passed. Most of us have had the experience of being angry and absolutely certain of our rightness, only to regret what we have said later when we have calmed down and thought about the matter. So there is no point in arguing with an angry person – adult or child. A rational response will only be achieved when the thinking brain is back in functioning mode and this requires a cooling off period.

Managing Anger
Staying Cool

When we are angry, a range of changes occur in our bodies:

- Heart rate rises.
- Blood flow to the muscles increases.
- Blood flow to the gut and many other organs goes down.
- Blood pressure rises.
- Blood glucose goes up to provide a quick source of energy.
- Breathing is faster.
- Muscle tension increases.
- Many hormones are released.
- Pupils dilate.

Of all the responses to anger listed above, two of them are within our conscious control. If we manage to control them, it seems that it is harder for the rest to get off the ground. The two responses are breathing and muscle tension. There is a two-way relationship between mind and body. Becoming angry or anxious increases muscle tension and speeds up breathing, but relaxing muscles and slowing breathing calms down the angry/anxious mind.

The 4–6 technique is a good way to slow your breathing down. It requires the *out* breath to be longer than the *in* breath – you count up to 4 as you breathe in and up to 6 as you breathe out. Try it yourself and notice the calming effect this sort of breathing has on your body. For muscle relaxation, it is best to initially focus on relaxing the muscles of the stomach and shoulders and then to spread this relaxation to other areas of the body. The whole calming down process is helped by co-ordinating long slow breathing out with the easing of tension in the muscles.

Using Mind Control

When someone has calmed down after an angry outburst, it is not a good idea to go through the episode again. Getting the pupil to describe it, will only re-awaken the same physical and emotional

sensations that accompanied the original outburst. An angry person needs to move on and one very effective way of doing this is by using the power of the mind to control feelings. The human mind has a unique ability for self-observation and utilising this is a powerful way of understanding ourselves and controlling our emotions. Thus developing 'sensible self-talk' and disassociating from an angry self by 'giving your anger a name', can both become important aspects of an anger management toolkit.

Furthermore, images and memories can be utilised to change feelings and behaviour. For instance, appropriate responses to situations can be rehearsed in the imagination or particular memories, sights or sounds can be evoked to calm the mind. This involves using the mind to control the mood, rather than allowing the mood to control the mind.

Developing Insight

Identifying the circumstances that commonly lead to anger can help in avoiding future angry outbursts. Similarly, considering the thought processes that often precede anger can reduce future flare-ups. The saying "The way we think influences the way we feel and act" is a very important insight for all of us to develop. Techniques like these encourage the angry child to understand his or her own anger and to appreciate how to forestall a loss of temper in future situations. The child then learns how to control events, rather than become the victim of circumstance.

Becoming Emotionally Intelligent

In an ideal society, emotional/social intelligence would be learnt by natural interactions between children and all their surrounding significant others: parents, siblings, other relations, neighbours, friends and teachers. However, as we all know, we do not live in a perfect world and many children come from environments that reinforce inappropriate behaviour. Furthermore, today's children, with access to television and video games, spend less time than previous generations socially interacting with others. So schools have to be more overt in teaching children emotional and social skills that they often lack. Anger management is one such skill.

Section 7 Dealing with an Angry Child

Notes for Tutor Worksheet

Dealing with angry children is a common enough experience for all teachers. **Stepping Down the Anger** offers a simple way of diffusing anger and preparing the pupil to move on in an appropriate way.

First you need to get the pupil to listen to you. This is done by voice tone and by a simple expression of understanding. In doing this you are gaining some initial rapport with him/her. The next step is to take the child out of fight mode. You begin by now lowering your own voice tone and also by showing you recognise that he/she has a problem that needs discussing. Again, you are affirming your understanding of their predicament. To complete the process you need to help the child to physically relax their body. Getting them to slow down their breathing and to loosen up their muscles does this.

Notes for Pupil Worksheet
(You may need to scribe for the pupil)

How Angry were You and Why? An anger outburst could be the result of a one-off occurrence or it could be part of a wider problem. This worksheet is particularly important because it enables you to gain some insight into the incident and also to investigate the broader picture. It may well be that the child has flared up because he/she is used to using anger as a means of achieving desires. But it should not be forgotten that anger thresholds are lowered by stress. This can be of a physical nature such as lack of sleep, inadequate diet or illness. Or it could be that the child has a short fuse because they are trying to deal with emotional problems at home or with friends. The picture that emerges from your discussion with the pupil will obviously determine whether you deal with anger control as the primary problem or whether you decide to use other units of the Behaviour Management Toolkit to address other difficulties.

7.1 Tutor Worksheet: Stepping Down the Anger

A suggested approach for dealing with an angry child

Note: *The rate at which you go through these steps will vary according to the level of anger.*

- ❖ **Use your voice**
  Raise the level of your voice to just under the level of that used by the angry pupil.

- ❖ **Express understanding**
  Show that you understand the pupil's anger without agreeing with their reason for being angry.
  e.g. *"Joe, I really understand that you are angry.*
  I really do understand. I can see that you are angry."

- ❖ **Begin to calm**
  Pause for a moment.
  Then, bringing the voice down a level say:
  "But you do need to calm down so we can talk about it."
  If possible, get the pupil to sit down. A glass of water may also help the calming process.

- ❖ **Slow down the breathing**
  Relax their breathing using the 4–6 technique,
  e.g. *"Now, Joe, I want you to slow down your breathing.*
  Spend longer breathing out, than breathing in.
  Count up to 4 as you breathe in, and count to 6 as you breathe out. Try this, using slow deep breaths."

- ❖ **Relax the muscles**
  Systematically, help the student to relax his/her muscles, co-ordinating this with their breathing. Do this sensitively by pacing the relaxation to the level of the anger.
  e.g. *"Now Joe, it will help you to lose your anger if you just relax the muscles in your body. So, as you breathe out, relax the muscles in your shoulders. Really feel those muscles sinking down as they relax. Now, as you breathe out, relax the muscles of your stomach..."*
  (Continue with head, neck, forehead, tongue, jaw, arms, and legs.)

- ❖ **Move on**
  Of course, it is necessary to investigate the causes of the anger outburst. However, do not get the pupil to re-live the incident that caused the problem. Instead, use the following worksheets to help them move on and manage future incidents more effectively.

7.2 How Angry were You and Why?

On a scale of 0 (calm) to 10 (furious) circle the number that shows how angry you felt.

This is how angry I felt:
0   1   2   3   4   5   6   7   8   9   10
calm   furious

I was on _____ because _____

_____

_____

- ❖ Were you feeling angry **before** the incident?   **yes / no**
- ❖ Were you feeling angry **before** you came to school today?   **yes / no**
- ❖ If you answered "yes" to either of the above questions, can you say why you were angry? Explain below, if you can?

_____

_____

- ❖ How long did you sleep last night? _____
- ❖ What did you have for breakfast/lunch? _____
- ❖ Have you fallen out with someone close to you? _____

The worksheets in this unit will help you to understand more about your own anger and how to control it.

Section 8 Assessing the Anger

Notes for Pupil Worksheet
(You may need to scribe for the pupil)

This Really Winds Me Up! is essentially a diagnostic tool, which will help you to analyse the basis of the student's anger. Every pupil should complete all the worksheets in the basic programme. But responses on this worksheet will enable you to identify individual problems and guide you to additional worksheets.

Responses tend to fall into five different categories:

1 Not taking responsibility

2 Not being able to accept criticism

3 Righteous anger

4 Attention-seeking

5 Response to bullying

After the student has completed **This Really Winds Me Up!**, it will be necessary to have a short counselling session to assess the pattern of answers. For instance, getting angry in response to being told off could be due to an inability to accept criticism, not being able to take responsibility for his/her own actions or simply righteous anger if they had been told off for something that someone else had done. Getting them to give examples of the ones they have ringed will enable a quick assessment of the reasons for their anger and enable you to decide on suitable extra worksheets.

8.1 This Really Winds Me Up!

If any of the following has made you **a bit angry in the past**, ring them *once*.

If any of the following has made you **really mad in the past**, ring them *twice*.

People saying things about my family	Being told off	Being called a liar
Being criticised	People taking my things	Being ignored
Being blamed for something I didn't do	Being teased	People breaking my things
My work getting messed up	Being pushed	People showing off
Losing	Not being believed	People calling me names	Seeing a fight
People not listening to me	People asking me lots of questions	People getting more attention than me
Getting things wrong	Being shouted at	

Anything else? Write them below.

Section 9 Basic Programme 1

Calming Down Techniques

The worksheets in this section of the programme can be used with all students. They will help you to explain what happens physically when someone gets angry and enable you to teach some useful techniques for staying calm and in control. Look through them before you start so that you, yourself, are familiar with the skills you will be teaching.

The worksheets in this section will help pupils in several ways. First they will become more aware of the effects of anger on their own bodies. Then they will learn how they can calm themselves down by consciously reversing two of these effects – muscle tension and rapid intake of breath. Finally, they will be taught to recognise the sort of thoughts that can trigger anger and how to challenge and change these thoughts.

Notes for Pupil Worksheets
(You may need to scribe for the pupil)

Understanding Anger provides a general introduction to what happens in the brain and body when someone gets angry. **Feel the Difference** continues this theme by making the pupil aware of his/her own physical experiences of anger. If they need prompting there is a list of these responses in the introductory tutor notes in this unit. Although we all have similar bodily responses to anger, our actual conscious experiences differ. So, whilst some people will be aware of tensions in the neck or shoulders, others may experience a particular sensation in the stomach. Being aware of how we personally experience anger can then be utilised in subsequent relaxation programmes. Similarly, the relationship of colour with mood is explored with a view to using this as part of a calming down process.

The 4–6 Way to Keep Calm explains a simple breathing technique that can be used to prevent an anger outburst. The over-breathing that occurs during anger and fear is a preparation for sudden strenuous muscular activity. Its effect not only ensures plenty of oxygen in the blood, but also lowers carbon dioxide levels. This in turn causes the acidity of the blood to change and makes the individual feel more excitable. Consciously slowing down the breathing will reverse this effect because a longer out breath allows the carbon dioxide to build up again. Inhalation also tends to be excitatory on the brain (think of the sharp in-breath when we are startled), whilst breathing out tends to be calming. There can even be a small increase in heart rate when we breathe in and a slowing down when we breathe out. With very deep breathing this can be clearly detected.

Stay in Control provides practise in muscle relaxation and breathing control. Once pupils have rehearsed this a few times, they should be able to use it independently to calm themselves down.

Listen to Your Thoughts gets pupils to understand the relationship between thought and mood. It's very important to explore the concept that 'The way I think influences how I feel' because anger doesn't just occur, particular types of thoughts precede it. These thoughts are invariably negative because they tend to personalise and magnify things. If pupils can be encouraged to challenge their initial thoughts and see other possible interpretations, then they are less likely to explode into anger.

Certain emotionally charged thoughts affect the way we feel and act. They tend to be automatic responses to situations. For instance, a criticism might lead to thoughts like 'She always picks on me' or 'I can't do anything right for him'. Successful anger management necessarily involves identifying and challenging the thoughts that trigger anger outbursts.

Try it for Yourself and **Thought Control**, the final two worksheets in this section, aim to teach the pupil a simple method of disputing and challenging their thoughts.

This set of worksheets introduces a range of calming techniques. To be effective in controlling and managing anger, they need to be practised on a regular basis until they become automatic responses to challenging situations.

9.1 Understanding Anger

To understand anger, you need to know a bit about how your brain works. So look at this diagram of the brain and then read the explanation below.

Brain showing the Limbic System (shaded area)

- ❖ The bottom part of your brain is called the **brain stem**. This controls the things that you do automatically like remembering to breathe, the speed at which your heart beats and so on.

- ❖ The outside layer of your brain is called the **cortex** and this is the part you use when you think about things.

- ❖ Underneath the cortex is the **limbic system**. This part of the brain deals with danger. If you were attacked by something, you wouldn't want to stand around thinking what to do. You would want to act quickly and either fight back or run away.

When you get angry, it's the limbic part of your brain that takes over. You act quickly without thinking. You are sure that you are right in what you are doing. You go into 'fight' mode.

- ❖ A message is sent to your brain stem to prepare your body.
- ❖ Your brain tells:
    - ❖ your heart to beat faster
    - ❖ your muscles to become tense
    - ❖ your blood pressure to rise
    - ❖ your breathing to become faster
    - ❖ your eyes to open wider and your pupils to become larger.

When you are angry, you are no longer in control of yourself. This anger management programme will help you to take back control and put the thinking part of your brain back into action.

© Hodder & Stoughton Ltd 2004. Copying permitted in purchasing school only.

9.2 Feel the Difference

On the grid below, describe the things that happen to your body when you're angry and then when you're calm. You may not need to fill in all of the boxes.

My	when I'm angry	when I'm calm
face	e.g. goes red, scowls	e.g. usual colour, relaxed
eyes		
teeth		
shoulders		
heart		
stomach		
breathing		
muscles		
legs/feet		
arms/hands		

Now fill in the following grid:

Where, in your body, do you first feel your anger?	These things help me to feel calm:
This is the colour of my anger:	**This is the colour of calm:**

9.3 The 4–6 Way to Keep Calm

❖ When we are angry, we tend to breathe in a short, sharp way. This prepares our bodies for fight mode.

❖ To keep calm and relaxed we need to slow down our breathing.

❖ Next time you feel yourself getting angry, try this:

> Slow down your breathing, take slow deep breaths.
>
> Breathe in and, as you do this, count to 4.
>
> Breathe out and, as you do so, count to 6.

❖ Practise this now. Notice how calm it makes you feel.

9.4 Stay in Control

Exercise 1 – Fade out the anger

❖ Colour this shape the colour of anger.

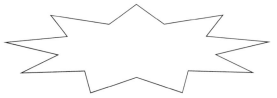

❖ Next read the following instructions:

Breathe slowly and deeply
Count 4 as you breathe in, 6 as you breathe out.
Relax your shoulders and stomach muscles.
Shut your eyes.
See the angry shape you have just coloured in.
Now let the colour become paler and paler.
As the colour fades, let the shape become
smaller and smaller until it finally disappears.

❖ When you have understood these instructions, practise them three times by yourself.

Exercise 2 – Cover yourself in calm

❖ Colour this shape the colour of calm.

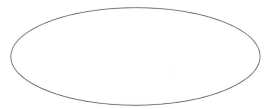

❖ Now read the following instructions:

Breathe slowly and deeply.
Count 4 as you breathe in, 6 as you breathe out.
Relax your shoulders and stomach muscles.
Shut your eyes.
See the calm shape you have just coloured in.
See it getting larger and larger until it gently
surrounds your whole body.

❖ When you have understood these instructions, practise them three times by yourself.

9.5 Listen to Your Thoughts

We all have an inner voice. Sometimes you can clearly hear what it's telling you and other times you are hardly aware of it. Here are some examples of the inner voice at work.

Can you see how what you say to yourself affects the way that you feel about things? Anger doesn't just happen. It happens because of the thoughts that go through your head. Look at the situations below and you'll see how anger outbursts can occur because of the way someone thinks.

9.6 Try it for Yourself

Think about a time that you were very angry.

What happened? _____

_____

_____

_____

What were your thoughts at the time? _____

_____

_____

_____

How strong was your anger?

annoyed   1   2   3   4   5   6   7   8   9   10   very angry

Think about the incident again. Challenge your thoughts. What evidence do you have to support these thoughts? Think of all the other explanations for this evidence. Write down some possible alternative thoughts below.

_____

_____

_____

How strong is your anger when you think these alternative thoughts?

annoyed   1   2   3   4   5   6   7   8   9   10   very angry

Can you see how your thoughts affect how you feel about things?

9.7 Thought Control

You have now learnt a way of making yourself less angry by controlling your thoughts. To do this well, you need to practise. Next time you feel yourself getting angry, try this out:

- Write down your thoughts.
- Measure your anger and record it.

On a scale of 1 to 10, I am:

    annoyed 1 2 3 4 5 6 7 8 9 10 really angry

Think about what happened again. First thoughts can be wrong. What evidence is there to support your first thoughts? Could there be other ways of explaining the evidence? Think hard. Be prepared to challenge and dispute your thoughts.

- Write down all the other possibilities.
- Measure your anger again.

On a scale of 1 to 10, I am:

    annoyed 1 2 3 4 5 6 7 8 9 10 really angry

Has it gone down? If not try again. Look at the evidence again. Weigh up all the possibilities. Consider everything before you jump to conclusions!

Section 10 Basic Programme 2

Distancing the Anger

Some people are ruminators. They constantly mull over bad events and by doing this they re-live and intensify their initial unpleasant experiences. They are in a vicious circle, unable to detach themselves from events, actions and feelings. The following four worksheets will help pupils who fall into the rumination trap to distance and separate themselves from their angry thoughts.

Notes for Pupil Worksheets
(You may need to scribe for the pupil)

The first worksheet, **Talk to Your Anger**, helps pupils to view their own anger as a distinct and separate part of themselves. Doing this, will enable them to recognise that they also have a calm, rational self that can weigh up situations in a realistic way and offer sensible solutions to problems.

Bin Those Angry Thoughts is a simple and commonly used technique to end rumination by getting the pupil to write their angry thoughts down and then destroy them. It is a physical way of ending the constant chewing over of angry thoughts, thus allowing the pupil to move on. **Still Angry? – Write It Down** enables the pupil to externalise and express angry feelings in the form of a letter. Whether the letter should be sent or not could be a useful area of discussion.

10.1 Talk to Your Anger

❖ It's a good idea to distance yourself from your anger and one way to do this is to give it a name. It's not you, it's *Fred?, Sanita?, Nick?, Milly?...*

❖ This is the name of **my** anger:

❖ When you want to think about an angry situation, try doing it like this:

- Find 2 chairs.

- Sit down on one of the chairs and tell your anger to sit down on the other one. (Don't forget to call your anger by his/her name.)

- Ask your anger (using his/her name) to explain:

  What happened?   **When**?   **Who** else was there?
  Why did it happen?   **Which** things particularly annoyed you?

- Give your anger (again, use his/her name) some good advice on the best ways to deal with the situation.

- Make the advice even clearer by writing it down.

© Hodder & Stoughton Ltd 2004. Copying permitted in purchasing school only.

10.2 Bin Those Angry Thoughts

Angry thoughts are not usually very helpful.

A good way to rid yourself of them is to simply BIN THEM!

If you have any angry thoughts at the moment:

Write them down on a piece of paper.

Now, screw them up and

BIN THEM!

10.3 Still Angry? – Write it Down

When you feel angry with someone, try explaining your feelings in a letter. You don't have to send it, but it's a good way of saying what you are thinking. This will help you to get things out of your system in a calm way.

Dear _____,

        I just want you to know how angry I feel about _____

_____

_____

_____

_____

_____

_____

_____

_____

Perhaps we could meet sometime to talk this through.

Section 11 Basic Programme 3

Being Assertive

Students have already learnt techniques for stepping down their anger and distancing themselves from their angry feelings. So now it's time to teach them how they can communicate their wishes, needs and feelings without losing their temper.

Notes for Pupil Worksheets
(You may need to scribe for the pupil)

Be Assertive and **Cards** provide a clear strategy for the pupil to present his/her feelings about a situation in a calm and reasonable way. It would be useful to follow up discussion of these worksheets with some role-plays involving assertive ways of dealing with conflict situations. You may also find the following useful:

Worksheets 16.2 and 16.3 (in Unit 4 *Peer Relationships*).
All worksheets from Section 6 (in Unit 2 *Conflict Resolution*).

Assertiveness, as opposed to aggressive, manipulative or submissive behaviour, is recognised today as the most appropriate behaviour between adults at work and many companies and organisations provide courses on assertive behaviour for employees. It involves communicating in a calm, open and honest way regardless of the nature of the communication. The body language used also needs to be open, to match what is being said. Assertive behaviour recognises the rights of self and others.

Several copies of **Staying on Track** should be made so that the pupil can record how he/she deals with conflict situations. It is important to encourage the student to practise the techniques learnt in this course and to discuss which things work best. After completing the programme, several extra sessions should be set aside to monitor progress.

11.1 Be Assertive

- ❖ In the previous sessions, you have learnt about ways of controlling your anger. But anger only happens because you haven't worked out a better way of sorting out your problems.

- ❖ What you really need to do is to make your feelings known without losing your temper. If you can do this, you will be acting *assertively*.

- ❖ Next time you come up against a problem, don't lose your temper, instead follow the steps below. These will help you to sort things out assertively.

Who?
(Decide to whom you need to talk about the problem)

⬇

When and where?
(Decide on the best time and place to talk things through)

⬇

What?
(Explain clearly what you are annoyed about)

⬇

How?
(Practise saying things politely and calmly)

⬇

Listen?
(Allow other people to say how they feel about the problem)

⬇

Find?
(Find a solution that everyone feels reasonably comfortable with)

© Hodder & Stoughton Ltd 2004. Copying permitted in purchasing school only.

11.2 Cards

Use the boxes below to plan an assertive way of dealing with the situation.

1 **What** is making me angry?	**2** **Who** can I talk to about this?
3 **When** will be a convenient time to do this? **Where** would be a convenient place to discuss it?	**4** **How** should I talk about my feelings?
5 Listen	**6** Find an agreeable solution

Cut the boxes out and stick them onto card. Keep these cards with you and use them whenever you feel annoyed about something.

11.3 Staying on Track

Over the next week, keep track of the times when you could have lost your temper, but managed to control yourself. Notice the anger control techniques that worked well for you.

The problem.	
My first thoughts about things.	
What I did to calm myself.	Muscle relaxation? 4–6 breathing? Thought challenging? Talked to my anger?
How I distanced myself from my angry feelings.	2 chairs? Bin? Letter?
How I made my feelings known in an assertive way.	
What I did to take my mind off the problem and move on.	
The things that worked best for me in this situation.	

© Hodder & Stoughton Ltd 2004. Copying permitted in purchasing school only.

Section 12 Additional Worksheets

The worksheets in this section should be used alongside the assessment made in Section 8, 'Assessing the Anger'. Look back at the pupil's responses on Worksheet 8.1, **This Really Winds me Up!** Decide whether any particular individual problems need addressing and then choose from the following worksheets, as appropriate.

(1) Taking Responsibility
Learning to take responsibility is part of the process of growing up and accepting accountability for our own behaviour is an important aspect of this. The first four worksheets focus on acknowledging that we can choose the way in which we behave. They also emphasise the importance of learning to see situations through other people's eyes rather than attributing blame. It would be useful at this point to remind the pupil that they have already learnt a number of techniques for controlling their angry feelings and behaving more assertively. So if they allow themselves to react angrily to situations, they are choosing not to use the skills that they have already acquired.

Notes for Pupil Worksheets
(You may need to scribe for the pupil)

"You Made Me Angry" focuses on the importance of individual choice in the way in which we express our feelings. **Using 'Should'** encourages students to see situations through the eyes of others as well as their own, a theme that is then continued in the next worksheet with a tutor script.

Notes for Tutor Worksheet

What Do You Think? Before using, read this script through carefully. If you do decide to use it, make sure that you have the appropriate number of chairs available and that you are in a place where roles can be acted out privately. At the end of this session reinforce the idea that how the student thinks about a situation has a very important effect on his/her own feelings and actions ('The way you think influences the way you feel and act'). If you feel that it would be useful to develop this idea further, use some of the worksheets in Unit 5 *Mood Management*.

Notes for Pupil Worksheets
(You may need to scribe for the pupil)

Taking Responsibility again encourages pupils to think about and record how they handle conflict situations in terms of taking some responsibility themselves rather than simply blaming others. Several copies should be made of this monitoring sheet and time should be set aside to track progress.

(2) Dealing with Criticism

Everyone makes mistakes in life and part of growing up is accepting and learning from those errors. However, some people always see criticism as threatening. They perceive it as a personal attack on themselves, which needs to be fended off. They go into fight mode and anger takes over.

The next two worksheets focus on two important issues that will enable pupils to begin to develop a more mature attitude to dealing with criticism. The first, **Don't Pick on Me!**, teaches the pupil to challenge his/her initial thoughts about a perceived criticism. It shows the pupil that the more we personalise criticism, the more we feel threatened by it. An important part of growing up is to be able to detach our feelings about ourselves from our behaviour. After all, we cannot change ourselves, but we can change our behaviour. So criticism of a behaviour is far less threatening. Being able to accept valid criticism is a sign of self-confidence and maturity and the student needs to learn this important concept.

The second worksheet **Handling Criticism** gives the student a stepped approach to dealing with future situations where they feel threatened by criticism. Before using this worksheet, it would be useful to have some initial discussions with the pupil about the sort of issues that could be accepted as valid criticism and the ones that are unacceptable.

(3) Attention-Seeking

Parents and teachers can often feel confused about the child who seems to have an insatiable desire for attention. The sort of child who, when given attention, still says, "You never help me!" or "I always get left out". This problem is not about how much actual attention the child is getting but about his or her perceptions of the situation. It is as if their awareness of the actual situation is filtered through a hot thought that always says, "I do not get enough attention". Consequently these children often act in ways that are guaranteed to attract attention – they do something silly or unpleasant and get angry when reprimanded. The solution is not to give more attention but to change the child's perception when attention is given.

The following worksheets do two things. **Chloe's Problem** identifies the sort of thinking that leads to negative ways of demanding attention. Whilst the concept of having some **Special Time** offers a simple solution – focused attention that is recognised by the child as something special for him or her.

When helping a student to negotiate special time, it is important to note that 'special time' does not have to be lengthy, it can be as short as ten minutes a day. But the recipient does have to be the centre of attention during this time and it does have to be given on a regular basis.

(4) Anger Resulting from Bullying

For additional worksheets relating to bullying, see the appropriate sections in Unit 4 *Peer Relationships*.

12.1 "You Made Me Angry"

> When you were very young, adults wanted to protect you from harm, so they told you what to do and what not to do. For instance, they probably told you not to run into the road or eat things that could harm you.
>
> As you get older, people expect you to take more responsibility for your own actions and behaviour.
>
> Sometimes when people get angry, they blame other people for their anger. When they do this, they are **not taking responsibility for their own behaviour**.
>
> When you feel annoyed about something, you can choose whether to deal with it in an angry way or find another, more mature, way of expressing your opinion.
>
> Remember, nobody **makes** you react in an angry way. You can **choose** to be angry. On the other hand, you can choose to make your feelings known in a more appropriate way.

Now think about a time when you got angry and explain to your tutor what happened.

_____

_____

Do you feel that someone else was to blame for your anger? _____

If you wrote 'yes', who do you think was to blame and why? _____

_____

_____

Now think about the situation again.

Other people can irritate you or annoy you, but can they really force you to be angry?

Think about the earlier work that you have done on anger management.

Could you have acted differently? Would that have made a difference to the outcome of the situation?

_____

_____

12.2 Using 'Should'

People often get angry because they don't try to see things from anyone else's point of view. They then say things like:

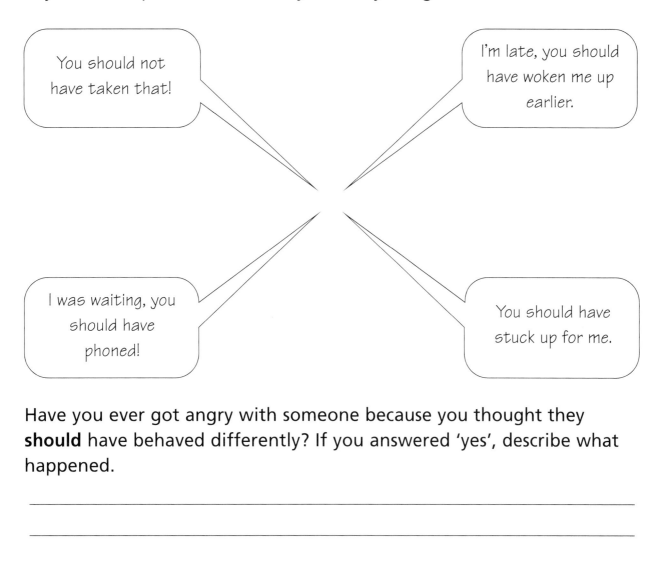

Have you ever got angry with someone because you thought they **should** have behaved differently? If you answered 'yes', describe what happened.

_____

_____

_____

Did you ask them to explain why they had acted in the way they did?

Did you try and look at the situation from their point of view?

Could this have made a difference to the way you felt about things?

Would it have made a difference to the other person?

So next time you feel angry:

Stop   *Ask*   *Listen*   *Think*

12.3 Tutor Worksheet: What Do You Think?

- Arrange 3 chairs like this:

- Sit on chair 1

    Think about a time when you were angry with someone.
    Describe what happened.
    - How did the situation arise?
    - What actually happened?
    - What were your thoughts at the time?
    - What were your feelings at the time?
    - What did you do?

- Sit on chair 2

    Now imagine that you're not yourself, but the person with whom you were angry.
    Describe what happened from his/her viewpoint.
    - How did the situation arise?
    - What actually happened?
    - What were your thoughts at the time?
    - What were your feelings at the time?
    - What did you do?

- Sit on chair 3

    You are now an outsider. You are thinking about what happened between the two people in front of you.
    Give a balanced view of the conflict between these two people. Describe what happened from both points of view.
    Explain how each person felt.
    How did this affect the way they acted?

- Sit back on chair 1

    You are yourself again.
    Think again about the situation. Could you have acted differently?

12.4 Taking Responsibility

Over the next week, keep track of any time when you chose to control your anger by taking responsibility for your actions and by listening to others.

What was the problem?	
What I did instead of losing my temper.	
What the other person said about his/her side of the story.	
My views.	
Was the problem eventually sorted out? How?	

12.5 Don't Pick on Me!

No one likes being criticised, but some people handle it better than others. Here are two examples:

Situation	Thought	Feeling	Action
"Your room is really untidy, Joe. Clear it up!"	She's always on at me!	?	?
"Stop talking Yasmin and get on with your work!"	Suppose I was talking loudly. Better get some work done.	?	?

Can you see how Joe has turned his mum's criticism into a personal attack? He doesn't think she's criticising the state of his room, he thinks she's getting at him **personally**. So he now starts to feel threatened and begins to lose his temper.

Yasmin, on the other hand, thought she was being criticised for what she was doing. She didn't feel that it was an attack on her as a person. So, unlike Joe, she didn't feel threatened by the teacher's criticism and was able to handle the situation.

Next time someone criticises you, ask yourself this question:

"Is this a criticism of me as a person or is it a criticism of my behaviour?"

12.6 Handling Criticism

Try using these five steps next time you're in a situation where you feel threatened by a criticism.

Step One

> Stop!
>
> Use 4–6 breathing. Relax your muscles.

Step Two

> Ask Yourself!
>
> Is this a criticism of me or is it a criticism of my behaviour?

Step Three

> Not sure?
>
> If you don't understand the criticism ask for more information.

Step Four

> If it is true, agree with it.
>
> Think what you should do next.

Step Five

> If it is untrue, say quietly but firmly,
>
> *"I am unhappy about what you have said because it is not true."*

If you feel annoyed, calm yourself and handle the situation by using some of the techniques you have already learnt in this anger management course.

12.7 Chloe's Problem

This is Chloe. She often gets angry because she feels that no one takes much notice of her. Then when she's cross, she sometimes does silly things and unfortunately these often get her into trouble. Getting into trouble makes her feel even angrier. Chloe thinks there is no solution to her problems, but there is. She needs to negotiate some **Special Time**.

If you ever feel like Chloe, this is what you should do:

❖ List the people who you feel should give you more attention.

❖ Arrange a discussion time with each person on your list. This should be at a convenient time and place for both of you.

❖ During your discussions, ask each person to help you to arrange some 'special time'. This is personal time that they can give you on a regular basis. Don't expect too much. A short amount of personal time, which you can count on, is what will make the difference.

❖ Sorting out these meetings by yourself might be a bit difficult, so get someone to help you. (Your tutor? A friend? Your mum?...)

❖ The next worksheet might be useful in planning how you do this.

12.8 Special Time

I am going to meet with:

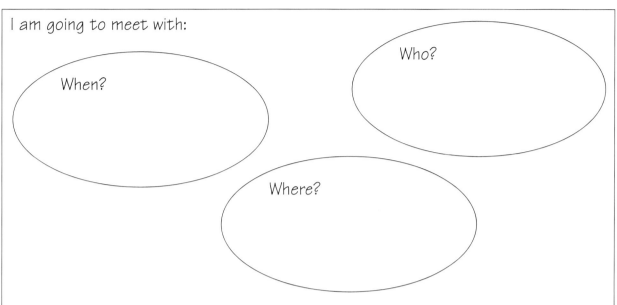

Here are some suggestions I have for 'special time'

When	Where	What

This is the special time we have both agreed to:

When	Where	What

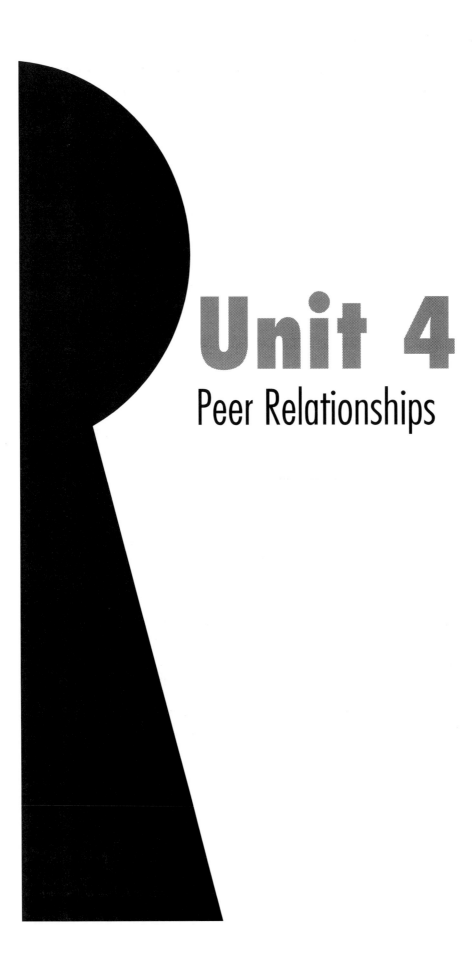

Unit 4
Peer Relationships

Tutor Notes – Introduction

Note: Low self-esteem can be a barrier to the forming of good peer relationships. If the student with whom you are working has a poor sense of self worth, it may be helpful to first work through the self-esteem section in Unit 5 **Mood Management**.

This unit contains sections on bullying. **If you have a bullying situation that needs addressing immediately please go to the Tutor Worksheet 17.1.**

Being able to form good relationships is essential for happiness: failure in this area can lead to a range of other difficulties including academic problems. Yet the skills needed for friendship are not normally taught. Rather, it is expected that children will automatically absorb these abilities through mixing with others. Some clearly do, but others don't.

There are many indications that the capacity for forming good and lasting relationships has, like most other abilities, both inherited and learnt components. Some children have an almost inborn ability to read the body language and facial expressions of others and can instinctively respond in suitable ways. However, these skills are also clearly helped by having a loving family and parents who can give the right guidance. But not everyone is lucky enough to have these abilities naturally and what's more, some children are not given good guidance on how to form strong and lasting relationships.

The theme followed in this unit is, once again, 'The way I **think** influences the way I feel and act'. So, in *Peer Relationships* students will be taught to recognise how their own thoughts, feelings and actions determine how their peers feel and act towards them.

Structure of the Course

The first section **Relationships** looks at definitions and ensures that the pupil understands the nature and language of relationships. This is followed in Section 14 by **Friends**, an analysis of friendship skills and an outline of ways in which skills in this area can be improved. The third section **What is Bullying?** looks at the nature of bullying while Section 16 **Dealing with Bullying** teaches a range of behaviours and strategies aimed at coping with, and stopping bullying. Clearly the ideal is to get the pupil who is a bully to change his/her behaviour and Section 17 **Bullies Can Change** deals with this process, as well as having suggestions for the tutor about how to deal immediately with a mobbing situation. Finally, how to resist negative **Peer Pressure** is the subject of the last section.

This unit addresses a number of areas such as difficulties in establishing friendships, problems relating to bullying and dealing with peer pressure. Whilst Section 13 will be useful for all students, tutors will need to be selective in using other parts of the unit.

Section 13 Relationships

This section is educational and helps the pupil to think about and define the nature of his/her relationships with peers and those in authority.

Notes for Pupil Worksheets
(You may need to scribe for the pupil)

You and Your Peers defines the concept of a peer and asks the pupil to identify his/her peer group.

The next four worksheets investigate the concept of power, in both its positive and negative aspects. **Peers and Power** defines friendship as a relationship where power is balanced. **Look at how Powerful I am** then asks the pupils to look at the positive side of power in their own lives – their personal sense of empowerment. **Power and Authority** goes on to examine the justified use of power in terms of authority. With teenagers, this will clearly be an interesting area for discussion! **Power and Domination** then pulls together the ideas developed in the previous three worksheets and asks the students to consider the darker side of power – the desire to dominate.

There are a lot of important concepts in this section, so don't rush, spend time talking through the ideas and examining the student's own perspective and experiences on these matters.

13.1 You and Your Peers

Your **peers** are people like you. They are the kind of people who are in your class or year group. They are similar in age to you and have probably had lots of the same sorts of experiences.

Think about your own peers. Some of these will be **friends** or even close friends. Others will be people you know quite well and although you might talk to them or do things with them, you don't call them friends. These peers are your **acquaintances**. Finally, there are probably peers in your school or neighbourhood who you know vaguely, but have little to do with. Show your own **peer group** by filling in some names below.

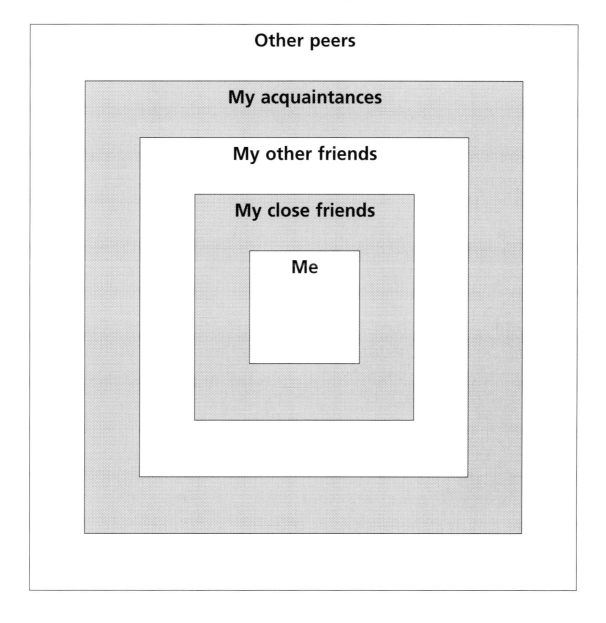

13.2 Peers and Power

Have you ever asked yourself why you feel comfortable with some of your peers and not with others? The ones you feel most comfortable with are probably your friends. They are the people with whom you:

❖ feel on the same level;

❖ give and take;

❖ have an equal say in things; and

❖ have things in common.

You feel equal in your relationships with your friends. You know your friends will not try to put you down because they are not trying to be more powerful than you. You and your friends get on well because you respect each other's abilities and although you may compete, you only do this in a friendly way.

In the box below describe a good friend and explain the ways in which your relationship is comfortable.

```
┌─────────────────────────────────────┐
│                                     │
│                                     │
│                                     │
└─────────────────────────────────────┘
```

Uncomfortable relationships are not balanced friendships because within them, power is unequal in some way. If you can, use the box below to describe a peer relationship which you find uncomfortable.

```
┌─────────────────────────────────────┐
│                                     │
│                                     │
│                                     │
└─────────────────────────────────────┘
```

Power is not just one thing. Used in the right way, it is a very positive part of everyone's life, but there are also kinds of power that are unhelpful and get in the way of good peer relationships. Over the next few worksheets we'll be looking a bit more closely at power. This will help us to sort out which types of power are OK and which are not.

13.3 Look at how Powerful I am

Power is the ability, energy and strength to do things. It's something we all need and value.

Think about yourself. You have the power to do lots of things. Some of these might be quite simple; others might be more special to you. Just to remind yourself of your own power, try writing about your own abilities, skills, talents and strengths anywhere in the box below. You might like to add some illustrations.

13.4 Power and Authority

Power also has another meaning. It can mean to have **authority** (to be in charge, to have the right to make decisions). Your parents or guardians are in charge of looking after you. When you were younger, other people made lots of decisions for you. As you have grown older, you have probably started to make more decisions for yourself.

List the sort of decisions your parents/guardians still make for you. Beside them, list some of the decisions you make together and some that you now make for yourself.

Some of the decisions my parents/guardians still make for me	Things we decide together	Some of the decisions I now make for myself

Who else has authority over you? _____

What sort of decisions do they make for you? _____

Do you have authority over anyone else? _____

If you do, what sort of decisions do you make for them? _____

13.5 Power and Domination

✓ The power to use your abilities, talents and skills is good and positive. It helps you to develop into an interesting and thoughtful person.

✓ The power of authority that your parents and teachers have is usually acceptable. As you get older, you may challenge some of that authority, but you also probably recognise that some decisions made by other people can be in your best interests.

✗ But there is a third type of power that is not acceptable. This is the power that is used to **dominate** or **control** other people. It is the power that is used to **force** people to do things against their own interests or wishes. This is the sort of power that makes relationships uncomfortable.

Has anyone ever tried to dominate you or force you to do something? Have you ever come across situations where this sort of power has been used against other people? Write about your experiences below.

Who was involved?	What happened?

Section 14 Friends

The aim of this section is to teach the basic skills of friendship:

        listening   **empathy**   **respect**
        praise   **reliability**   **simply talking**

Although the first step is to introduce these six skills, it is unlikely that students will be able to become proficient just by going through the worksheets. Some will need to be demonstrated and role-play will be the best method for this. Others will require careful discussion to emphasise the points being made. Before you start, read through the worksheets yourself and think about how you can put these ideas across.

Notes for Pupil Worksheets
(You may need to scribe for the pupil)

My Friends allows the pupil to talk about their current friendships and think about how these contribute to his/her quality of life.

Friends Listen introduces the importance of learning to listen to others and how to show them that you are listening. Listening skills particularly lend themselves to role-play. You could demonstrate good listening skills, then ask the student to listen whilst you describe something (perhaps a holiday, an outing, or an exciting football match). Whilst doing this, observe the pupil's body language and eye contact. Notice also how well he/she can reflect back the content of what you have been saying. This close observation will allow you to give detailed feedback so that in the next role-play you can see whether the student is actually making the effort to change. The main thing is to keep the pupil practising until things come right. Worksheet 6.3 in Unit 2 *Conflict Resolution* can also be used alongside this one.

Friends Show Empathy introduces a skill that is more difficult to put over, so a thorough discussion on empathy may be necessary. This may be particularly true when empathy is needed with a friend who is sad or unhappy. Here are some possible situations that could be used to introduce and emphasise the need for empathetic behaviour:

- Success – being happy for a friend who has done well.
- Failure – commiserating with a friend who has not done well.
- Unhappiness/Sadness – showing genuine sympathy to a friend who has fallen out with someone, has been bereaved or whose parents are getting divorced.

Friends Show Respect and **Friends Give Each Other Praise** follow on from a discussion on empathy; they show some of the ways in which empathy can be revealed.

Section 14: Friends

Friends Do What They Say emphasises the importance of reliability. It's easy to get out of an awkward situation by making promises that won't be kept. But whilst doing this can solve an immediate problem, the long-term consequence of behaving in this way is to hurt people's feelings and be labelled as untrustworthy. These are the basic ideas that need to be put across in discussions about this worksheet.

Friends Talk is the final worksheet in this section. With a friend, we feel comfortable in silence. Nevertheless, talking about common interests is very important and, for some children, knowing what to say is a problem. A useful interactive session with the pupil could involve just talking about the sorts of things that their peers are interested in, then encouraging them to acquire knowledge in those areas so that they can join in conversations. It should be emphasised to the pupil that this exercise is not about showing off their knowledge, but just to help them become part of the group. Work in this area can also be linked to earlier worksheets. It should begin to raise awareness that talking skills also need to involve other things like praise and being interested in the opinions of others. A single worksheet on 'talking' can only begin to introduce some of these ideas, so it's important to give the student a few challenges and to regularly discuss progress.

Depending on needs, one or several sessions may be required on each of these skills. At the end, it will also be necessary to set up some sort of **maintenance programme**, where you arrange to see the pupil at regular intervals to check progress and re-visit particular skills as required.

14.1 My Friends

Friendships are important in a lot of ways. They make you feel good about yourself. They're fun. They can help you to deal with stress and you can also learn a lot from friends. If you get good at making and keeping friends, you will probably enjoy good relationships with people throughout your life. So let's start with exploring some of your current friendships. Use the grid below to help you.

Friends ...	Who?	Describe a time they did this
make me laugh		
help me to feel secure		
explain things		
co-operate		
help me to deal with stressful situations		
work with me		
help me to deal with conflicts		
make me feel good about myself		
help me to sort out problems		

14.2 Friends Listen

When somebody really listens to you, it makes you feel good. That's why learning to listen is such an important part of friendship. But listening is not just about keeping quiet whilst someone else talks. It involves actively showing that you are hearing and thinking about what is being said. Here are some useful ways in which you can show that you are really paying attention and listening well.

- ❖ Face and slightly incline yourself towards the speaker.
- ❖ Make eye contact.
- ❖ Focus on what the speaker is saying.
- ❖ Use body language (nods, attentive noises etc.) to show that you are taking an interest and understanding what is being said.
- ❖ Be patient. Hear the speaker out.
- ❖ When you do speak, it's often useful to reflect back by summarising what has been said so far. This not only shows that you were listening, but also makes certain that you have actually understood correctly.
- ❖ Finally, don't rush in with advice or judgements. Just showing you were listening may be all that's required.

When you have been through and understood the points above, it's time for a bit of practice:

- ❖ Tell your tutor about something that really interests you. Whilst you're talking, your tutor will demonstrate good listening skills.
- ❖ Now listen to your tutor and show how well you can pay attention to what he or she is telling you.
- ❖ Finally, really practise these listening skills wherever you can.

14.3 Friends Show Empathy

When you show **empathy** towards someone you do two things:

> First you really **understand** what that person is actually feeling. We have lots of ways of describing this. Here are two of them. Empathy is like:
>
> *'Standing in someone else's shoes'*
>
> *'Looking through someone else's eyes'*
>
> Discuss these two phrases with your tutor. Make sure you really understand what they mean.
>
> Obviously, it's easy to know what someone is feeling if they tell you, but sometimes people don't want to talk about their feelings. A good friend will be able to spot clues. You can often tell what someone is feeling by their tone of voice, the expression on their face, the way they are standing/sitting etc. We call this **body language**.
>
> **Role-play** *(Your tutor can be your partner, or you might want to get someone else involved in this activity.)*
>
> One partner thinks of a feeling and tries to show it **just using body language**. The other partner has to guess the feeling and then demonstrate that feeling themselves, just using body language. Try it out a few times. Here are some feelings you could use:
>
> happy   sad   angry   annoyed   irritated   shy   frightened
> embarrassed   interested

> Secondly you must **show** that you understand why they feel that way. You do this by what you say, your tone of voice and also by your body language. So if someone is feeling sad, you will show empathy if you listen carefully to what they are saying, talk sympathetically and also show some sadness in your own face and body.
>
> A lot of the time, you probably do all this automatically, but the better that you become at showing empathy, the more people will want you as a friend.
>
> **Role-play** *(Again, your tutor can be your partner, or you might want to get someone else involved.)*
>
> One partner role-plays someone who is feeling strongly about something. This time, talk and use body language to explain the situation. The other partner's job is to show empathy by what they say and how they say it.

14.4 Friends Show Respect

Think about someone who shows you respect. Who is it? How does this person show their respect? How does it make you feel? Discuss this with your tutor and then write about it in the box below.

Now think about someone who has been disrespectful to you. Who is it? How does this person show their disrespect? How does it make you feel? Discuss this with your tutor and then write about it in the box below.

Being treated with respect makes you feel good whereas someone being disrespectful can make you feel hurt and angry. Discuss this point with your tutor. Are there any ways in which you could show more respect to your friends?

14.5 Friends Give Each Other Praise

Be generous with your praise. Complimenting your friends is a way of showing your friendship and of recognising your friends' efforts and achievements.

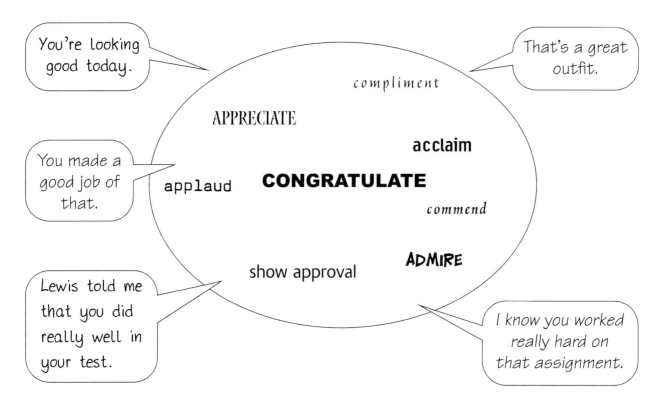

Praise strengthens the bond between you and your friends, but make sure that it's genuine. Insincere compliments are soon spotted and make the receiver feel uncomfortable.

Who praises you? Fill in the grid below.

Who?	For what?	It makes me feel...	It makes me think...

Who could you praise more? _____ _____ _____

14.6 Friends Do What They Say

Doing what you say makes you a strong friend.
People like to know where they stand.

But, if you do what you say, you have to be more careful about what you promise to do. It also means that sometimes you will have to find tactful ways of saying no. In the situation below, can you think of a considerate, but honest reply to the invitation?

Use the grid below to explore a time when you felt let down by someone not doing what he or she said they would. (Use a separate sheet if you need more room.)

Situation	My thoughts	My feelings

14.7 Friends Talk

Talking is good! It's part of friendship. But, be careful, you can also talk your way *out* of friendships. Here are some hints to help you to use talking in positive ways.

✓ **Friends find things in common**

> Yes, I enjoyed the new Harry Potter book as well. We could go and see the film together when it comes out.

Friends don't emphasise differences ✗

> Oh, you're in B2 are you? I'm in A1. I've always been clever.

✓ **Friends show they care . . .**

> How did your trip go last week? Tell me about it.

> Oh, you went on a trip. Next week I'm going on a fantastic visit to . . .

. . . and don't just talk about themselves ✗

✓ **Friends share their feelings**

> I'm really nervous about starting my new school.

With your tutor, make up some role-plays and practise some of these positive ways of talking to friends. Then, after the session, try out these skills. They will have a really positive effect on your friendships.

Section 15 What is Bullying?

The initial seven worksheets on bullying are educational. They explain the nature of bullying and what it includes. Before using these worksheets, look carefully through them. You might want to use them as the basis for getting either groups of students or individual pupils to appreciate what motivates bullies and what induces their victims to tolerate such aggravation. Or you may want to omit this section and go straight on to the practical worksheets. The practical section for pupils starts at Section 16.

Notes for Pupil Worksheets
(You may need to scribe for the pupil)

Bullying – What is it? is a particularly important worksheet because it presents a very wide picture of the nature of bullying. Use the word 'bully' and people often think of a powerful boy physically intimidating someone smaller and weaker. But bullying is much more insidious than this image suggests and includes many things that are easily missed by concerned adults.

Bullying – What Does it Include? extends and reinforces this more comprehensive description of bullying.

Who Gets Bullied? and **Why Put Up with it?** both focus on the victim side of bullying. Bullying is so rife that many pupils will have had first-hand experience at some time during their school life. It's important here to re-emphasise the point that anyone can become a victim of bullying and that suffering is not confined to a few odd or weak individuals.

Who are the Bullies? and **Mobbing** again help to widen the concept of bullying. Just as bullying is not just one thing, bullies themselves come in various guises. They can act individually but most often bullies take on different roles within group situations. Spend some time discussing the ideas and examples in these two worksheets. Many pupils will have aided a bully without necessarily admitting to themselves that that was the case. It is important that students do understand the nature of their actions within bullying scenarios.

Teasing is often a subtle way of bullying others. To all appearances it may seem to be simply playful and amusing but, beneath the surface, it can be a subtle way of discomforting and undermining another person's sense of well-being. Take some time to discuss this point with students.

15.1 Bullying – What is it?

A quarrel between friends is not bullying. Friends might disagree, say unpleasant things, even fight, but in their relationships they feel equal. Bullying is different. It is an **unequal** relationship where one person has power and the other person feels intimidated. Bullies are people who **deliberately** and **repeatedly** try to harm their victims.

A bully can gain power and intimidate another person in three ways. Here are the different types of bullying:

Physical	This is the most well-known sort of bullying because it's easy to see when someone has been physically hurt. It's generally boys who carry out most of the physical bullying and their victims frequently don't complain. They put up with it because lots of boys don't like to be seen as weak.
Verbal	Verbal bullying includes things like name-calling. It is less easy to spot because the hurt is not to the victim's body, but to their feelings. The harm it causes is just as real as physical bullying.
Indirect	Indirect bullying is often the most difficult to sort out because it often takes place within girls' friendship groups. When this happens, everyone seems to turn against one person. Because her friends are rejecting her, the victim feels alone, bewildered and helpless. Making someone feel rejected is a particularly powerful way to cause hurt.

Have you ever experienced any of these forms of bullying? If you have, explain what happened and how you dealt with it.

15.2 Bullying – What Does it Include?

There are lots of ways in which bullies can gain power over their victims. These include:

hitting	name-calling		tripping up
ignoring	racist remarks		threats
kicking	staring	insulting	biting
hiding someone's property		leaving someone out	
unpleasant gestures	scratching		taking property
ridiculing	spreading rumours		whispering
pushing	teasing		circulating nasty notes

Can you think of any more? _____

Read through the list again and put them into the correct column in the grid below.

Physical	✓	Verbal	✓	Indirect	✓

Have you ever been bullied? Tick any of these things that have happened to you. Explain what happened to your tutor.

15.3 Who Gets Bullied?

What sort of people get bullied? The answer is that, really, anyone can be bullied, but there are things that make a few people more at risk than others. Some of these are listed in the table below. Read them through and see if you can work out why. Put your answers in the second column. At the bottom, see if you can add any more ideas.

Things that might put people at risk of being bullied	Why?
Being the new boy/girl in school	
Being very shy	
Having a family that is over-protective	
Being different in some way (different skin colour or race, having learning problems, being very clever, having different interests etc.)	
Falling out badly with close friends	

15.4 Why Put Up with it?

People often put up with bullying for months and years without telling the people who could help them. To understand why they get themselves into this helpless position, you need to understand the thoughts and feelings of someone who is the victim of bullying. Read through the situations below. Fill in the empty boxes with your own ideas.

Situation	Thoughts	Feelings	Consequences
Jade and her friends constantly make comments about Sami's clothes and the way she looks.	**Sami**: I wish they'd leave me alone. I detest the way I look!	Shy Insecure Unconfident	Sami is often on her own. She finds it hard to mix with other people and has difficulty making friends.
Sanjay hangs around a group of lads he knew at primary school. They frequently taunt him about being poor at football. Sometimes Ben 'play fights' him and Sanjay gets hurt. He gives Ben money when he asks for it.	**Sanjay**: They all despise me because I'm such a wimp. I hate myself for always letting Ben take my money.		
Sarah used to be best friends with Lucy, Sanita and Yasmin. She had an argument with Lucy and now they all seem to have turned against her. In class, they pass round unpleasant notes about her. In the yard they pretend to ignore her, but often look her way and whisper and laugh.	**Sarah**:	Helpless Alone Rejected	

Now explain about a bullying situation that you know of. Who did it happen to? What actually happened? Can you guess the thoughts and feelings of the person who was bullied? What were the consequences?

15.5 Who are the Bullies?

There are lots of different reasons why some people become bullies. They may:

- come from a home where bullying is accepted and even encouraged;
- be bullied themselves and try to get their own back by picking on others;
- feel bad about themselves in some way;
- be angry and short tempered because things at home are difficult; or
- feel uncertain about their own friendships and therefore prop up their own position in a group by putting someone else down.

Can you think of any other reasons? _____

_____

One thing that is common to all bullies is that they want power over other people and this power is gained in unpleasant and unacceptable ways.

Bullies tend to fall into three distinct types:

1 **Aggressive bullies** who use physical force, or the threat of it, to scare victims. Bullies of this type often believe that aggressive behaviour is OK and hardly ever show feelings of regret for their actions.

2 **Manipulators** who are good at reading other people's minds and know just how their actions will hurt their victim. They get other people involved in things like whispering campaigns, isolating individuals or spreading rumours. Teachers often find it difficult to spot these sorts of bullies. Why do you think this is?

3 **Followers** who don't usually start things but quickly jump on board and join in once bullying has started.

Do you recognise these types of bullies? Perhaps you have been a victim or a witness of their activities. If you have, talk about your experiences to your tutor.

15.6 Mobbing

When a group bullies a person, it is usually called **mobbing**. One individual starts something off and then some people join in. Can you recognise any of these roles:

❖ The **assistants** quickly become involved and *help* the bully. They frequently think up new ways to step up the action and are often close friends with the person who starts things off.

❖ The **reinforcers** encourage the action by shouting *approval* and laughing. They egg on the main bullies and their assistants and often name-call the victim(s).

❖ The **outsiders** don't actually take part in the bullying, but neither do they show their disapproval of what's going on. They just *ignore* what's happening and tell themselves "This is none of my business."

❖ The **defenders** try to *stop* the bullying. They often comfort the person who has been bullied.

Below a bullying situation is described, showing the actions of different group members. Some boxes have been left empty for you to fill in.

Situation	Thoughts	Feelings	Type of Action
Mandy and her mates used to be friends with **Emily**. Then Emily was away on a holiday and when she came back she sensed that the group were not being friendly. In lessons they seemed to be whispering, laughing and passing notes. She felt that the comments were directed at her. One Monday morning she found that her locker had been broken into and her things vandalised. Soon after, Mandy came past. She gave Emily a long hard stare and then turned and smirked at her mates. Ruth then walked past and pushed Emily hard into the locker. Zoe laughed and said "You should see your face. You big cry baby." Sally just shrugged her shoulders and walked past. Hayley said "I think you should just leave her alone." She asked Emily if she would like to sit with her next lesson.	**Ruth** "Mandy's right, nobody likes Emily. We should teach her a lesson."	Powerful and...	Assisting
	Zoe	Excited and...	Reinforcing
	Sally "Glad it's not me! Anyway it's nothing to do with me. I don't want to get involved."		Ignoring
	Hayley		Defending

15.7 Teasing

Teasing between friends is gentle, friendly and good humoured. Everyone shares the joke and no one is made to feel uncomfortable.

But, teasing can also be aggressive. The person doing the teasing might find it funny, but the person on the receiving end may not share the joke. Here are some examples.

> Ben hides Michael's bag. He spends ages looking for it and in the end Michael misses his bus. Ben says "It was only a joke."

> Holly and her friends trick Anna into thinking that her mum has had an accident. Anna arrives home in tears to find that her mum is fine. Holly rings up Anna to laugh about the joke.

> Sanita gets a good mark in her test. John tells the teacher that she just copied the answers. When Sanita gets upset, he laughs and says "Can't you take a joke?"

Did you notice that the excuse for all of these activities is "It's OK because it's only a joke"? Bullies sometimes try to cover up their activities by claiming that they were just having a bit of fun. They pretend to be surprised that someone has got upset or angry.

It can be confusing to the person who has been teased – was it actually just intended to be a joke or was it really meant to cause hurt and upset? This uncertainty makes it more difficult to report teasing as bullying.

> **Remember:**
> **Teasing is only OK if everyone feels comfortable with the joke.**

Can you recall a time when teasing made you unhappy? If you can, talk to your tutor about what happened.

- ❖ What were your thoughts at the time?
- ❖ How did you feel?
- ❖ What did you do?
- ❖ Did you manage to make the person or people teasing you understand your feelings?

Section 16 Dealing with Bullying

Because the pupil you are dealing with may be frightened and intimidated by their experiences, quite a lot of sensitivity will be necessary when using the following worksheets. You may need to approach the ideas in this section slowly and with lots of reassurance.

Notes for Pupil Worksheets
(You may need to scribe for the pupil)

Be Assertive, **Look the Part** and **Sound the Part** all teach assertiveness. The core philosophy behind this is that if a person is open, honest and straightforward in his/her dealings with others, then it is reasonable to expect similar treatment in return. This confident way of dealing with people has to come over in what is said, how it is said and in the person's body language. It is the behaviour that is most likely to win the respect of others. It is clearly distinguishable from manipulative, submissive or aggressive behaviour.

Co-ordinating what is said with how a person looks and sounds is particularly important. For instance, it is no good speaking assertively if the body language is closed and defensive. To an observer this would instantly be recognisable as a lack of confidence. Similarly, speaking in an assertive way with jaw jutting forward would indicate aggression. Assertive body language is open and relaxed. The hands, if used, should be palms up and preferably symmetrical. Relaxing the shoulders, stomach, face and jaw muscles ensures a relaxed appearance and demonstrates confidence. Eye contact should be made but not held. Too little eye contact indicates a lack of confidence while too much will be recognised as aggressive. It is important that the voice is not raised since this would indicate an aggressive stance. Instead the voice should be even and firm and at the same level of loudness as would normally be used with a friend. Changing to this form of behaviour is not easy. A lot of role-play work may be necessary to help the pupil to co-ordinate what they say with how they look and sound and this may have to be repeated over several sessions.

Inside the Capsule uses the pupil's imaginative powers. The imagination can be a very potent tool and is frequently used by psychotherapists to help clients cope with difficult situations. The effect of teaching this technique is often two-edged. First it enables the taunted pupil to feel better than they have in the past in such situations; and second the fact that he/she is ignoring the taunts will tend to inhibit this behaviour in the perpetrators.

One of the most difficult problems is overcoming the culture of 'not telling' and it is obviously in a bully's interest to perpetuate this culture. The worksheet **Telling** is designed to start the process of discrediting the 'don't grass' tradition.

Change Those Thoughts, Thought Challenging and **Keep a Diary** are worksheets that the pupil can take away and use. It would be a good idea to provide several photocopies of these.

Putting it Together will help you to guide the student towards drawing up a personal plan of action for dealing with bullying situations. Spend some time discussing ideas and ways of doing this before finalising the plan.

16.1 Be Assertive

There are three ways of dealing with a problem. You can be:

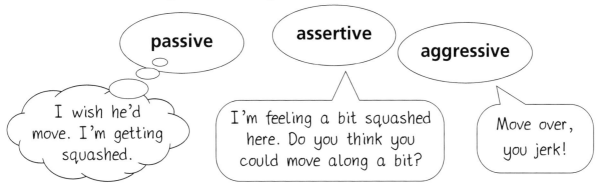

Passive people rarely get things to happen the way they want because they let others make decisions for them. **Aggressive** people are just the opposite, they demand and sometimes use force to get their own way. People who are **assertive** are firm and confident. They put over their own views, but also respect others.

Think back. Can you recall a time when you acted passively about something? Can you think of a time when you behaved aggressively with someone? Can you remember an incident where you were assertive? If you can, explain the situations to your tutor and then write about them below.

The Situation	What I Did	The Results
Passive		
Aggressive		
Assertive		

Acting assertively is a good way of dealing with bullying, but it takes practice. You need to prepare yourself to deal with problems in a calm way and learn how to act and speak with confidence. The exercises on the next few worksheets should get you started, but to become really assertive you must practise them regularly.

16.2 Look the Part

- The way you look
- How you stand
- The way you walk
- The expression on your face

These all give clues to your feelings. This is called **body language**. An assertive person uses their body language to make them look and feel confident. Here are some exercises for you to practise.

Role-Plays (Try these out with your tutor)

1. **Situation** — A boy comes up to you and demands your dinner money.

   Assertive Response — You look him in the eye, calmly say "I only have enough for my own dinner", turn round slowly and walk away in a relaxed manner.

2. **Situation** — A group of girls are staring at you and whispering about something.

   Assertive Response — [*Discuss your response with your tutor and then try it out.*]

3. **Situation** — A girl comes up to you and makes unpleasant personal comments.

   Assertive Response — [*Discuss your response with your tutor and then try it out.*]

Use a Mirror

At home, use a mirror to practise assertiveness. Think about a situation that works out well for you and try looking happy, confident, and pleased with yourself. Try standing in strong and confident ways.

Next imagine a challenging situation that you deal with assertively. Watch your body language in the mirror. Notice how good you feel when your body language is confident.

Now, keep practising!

16.3 Sound the Part

Assertive people not only *look* confident, they also *sound* sure about what they are saying. So, just as you might need to practise your body language, you may need to rehearse the way you sound. Here are some tips:

- Always remember, you have the right to say "no".
- Remember to say "no" firmly. Practise saying it to yourself in a determined way.
- Remember, if you say "no", you are just refusing a request. This does not mean that you are rejecting the person who asked you.
- If you're not sure about something, just say "I need more time".
- Suggesting alternatives can sometimes be helpful.

> No, I don't fancy going down by the river, let's play football instead.

> No, I don't want to go to Sarita's party. Let's go to the pictures instead.

- When you make a request about something, be clear about what you want. It may be helpful to practise before you actually do it.
- When you have made your request, don't allow anyone to side-track you. Stick to your point firmly until you receive a reply.
- Make sure that you don't get caught up in an argument. Speak calmly and firmly. If provoked, say "We'll talk about this later when tempers have cooled".

Discuss each of these points carefully with your tutor. Then try out some role-plays using the situations below.

1 A boy demands to use your mobile phone. How do you respond?	2 A good friend asks you to skip a lesson with her. You don't want to go. How do you deal with this?
3 A classmate asks to borrow your felt tip pens. Last time she borrowed them, some were missing and others didn't work.	4 A boy is blocking your way in the corridor. How do you get him to move?

16.4 Inside the Capsule

Dealing with taunts and insults can be difficult, so here's an idea.

- ❖ First imagine a space capsule that belongs to you and is just for your personal use.

- ❖ Only you can enter the capsule and you can leave it whenever you want.

- ❖ The walls of your capsule are incredibly strong, anything hitting them just shatters.

- ❖ Although you can still hear and see things, they don't affect you because nothing can get through these walls.

In the box, draw a picture of your capsule. Colour it in your favourite colours and put some things inside that will make it comfortable for you.

Next time someone tries to taunt you, just breathe slowly and deeply, call up your capsule and walk in. From the security of your capsule, you will be able to watch their words hit the outer walls and just blow apart, leaving you safe and sound.

Now get practising!

Use your imagination and go inside your capsule. Think of the worst thing that anyone could say to you. Watch the words hit the outer walls and smash to smithereens. Inside your capsule you feel calm, relaxed and confident.

16.5 Telling

"grass"   "cry baby"   "tell-tale"

These are the sorts of names that bullies and their followers regularly call people who report or complain about bullying.

Everyone knows it's wrong to harm or hurt other people. So bullies never want their activities to come out into the open and often go to great lengths to cover them up.

Unfortunately, their victims often support them in this. People who are bullied often keep quiet about what has been going on.

If you are bullied, you must report it.

❖ To get help, first think about the people who could help you.

Mum?   Dad?

Teacher?   ???

I've decided to talk about my problems to
_____

❖ Choose a moment when this person has time to listen.

When?

Where's the best place?

❖ Work out how you are going to explain the situation.

These are the main things that I am going to explain:

16.6 Change Those Thoughts

There are two main reasons why victims don't talk about their problems:

❖ **Fear**
People who get bullied often feel that telling will be useless because the bully or bullies are too powerful. They think that exposing the situation will only make things worse.

❖ **Shame**
Many victims are ashamed about what has happened. They feel humiliated because they haven't been able to defend themselves and even worse, they sometimes feel as if they are to blame for the bullying. They feel that if they were stronger, less different, better looking and so on, they would not be picked on.

The way to change negative feelings like fear and shame is to challenge the thoughts that produce them. Here are some examples of thoughts producing particular feelings and actions. Fill in the empty boxes at the bottom of the grid with your own ideas.

Thought	Feelings	Possible Actions
If I tell she'll only do something worse.	Low, pessimistic, helpless	Allow bullying to carry on.
I'm going to talk to my gran about this. She'll help me to sort it out.	Positive, hopeful	Start to find a solution.
Sean's mates are right. I never fight back. I'm just pathetic and feeble.		
Sean and his mates talk a lot of rubbish. I'm not weak, just too intelligent to play their games.		

Keep some copies of the next worksheet. Use them whenever you need to challenge negative or pessimistic thoughts.

16.7 Thought Challenging

These are my first thoughts about the situation:

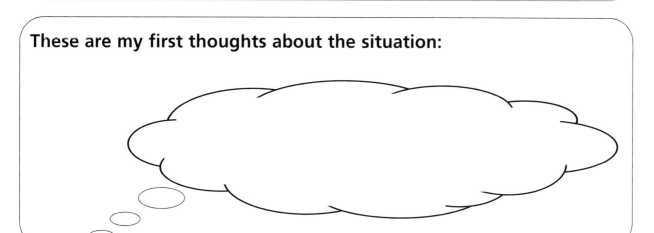

Hang on, there are better ways of thinking about this! Here are my thoughts now:

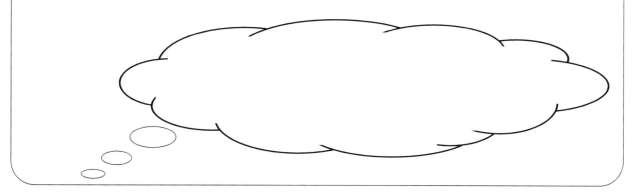

So, this is what I'm going to do:

16.8 Keep a Diary

You might find it useful to keep a diary of incidents, and then you'll be able to report things that happen accurately and in detail. But, be careful to keep the diary to yourself. Don't write it in public as this could provoke retaliation. Here is an example of how to keep a note of events. You might want to photocopy it and use this sheet or you may want to keep your notes in a book.

Date / Time: _____   Place: _____

Who was involved? _____
_____

What happened? _____
_____
_____
_____
_____

What I did: _____
_____
_____
_____
_____

16.9 Putting it Together

This unit has introduced you to lots of ways of dealing with bullying. Some you probably liked. Perhaps some are not for you. This worksheet will help you to plan your personal approach to sorting out those bullies.

This is the problem:

_____

_____

_____

This is my plan

1 _____

2 _____

3 _____

4 _____

Section 17 Bullies Can Change

Getting bullies to change can be extremely difficult because they are often unwilling to admit responsibility for their actions. This section starts with two tutor worksheets that aim to increase the pupil's own self-awareness and improve their ability to empathise with others.

Notes for Tutor Worksheets

The **Common Concern Method** is a way of dealing with mobbing situations. Its aim is to encourage empathy for a victim of bullying and at the same time generate solutions to the problem. This is not something that can be achieved in one session. It requires time and patience to implement and to maintain gains. Read this script through carefully before using it.

Dealing with Difficult Relationships is a powerful technique which is commonly used in psychotherapy to develop self-awareness and to improve understanding of the thoughts, feelings and concerns of others. Read it through carefully before trying it with a pupil. If you do decide to use this script, make sure that you are in a convenient place where other people will not disturb you.

Notes for Pupil Worksheets
(You may need to scribe for the pupil)

Once you feel that you have gained some sort of rapport with a pupil who has been involved in bullying, you may choose to develop this further by using the other two worksheets in this section. A student who has accepted responsibility for bullying needs to move on, the worksheet **Understand Yourself** begins this process. Resulting from a discussion of this worksheet you may decide to work with the pupil on one of the other units in this book.

Learn from Others develops the concept of using role models to assist the behavioural changes that are required.

17.1 Tutor Worksheet: Common Concern Method

(Method of dealing with 'mobbing' developed by A. Pikas)

After being informed about a 'mobbing' situation, the tutor should arrange to see each alleged bully **individually** for about 10 to 20 minutes. It's important to see the bullies before the victim. If the victim is seen first, he or she may have to re-enter the classroom to face accusations of 'having told'. This would also probably have the adverse effect of pulling the bullying group further together.

Stage 1 Get the bully talking

When interviewing each alleged bully, the tutor is trying to achieve a rapport with the student. A dominant relationship, where guilt was assumed and retribution likely to follow, would destroy this. The following words are suggested as an opening:

> I would like to talk to you because I've heard that xxxx has been having a hard time. What do you know about this?

Usually, the bully will say something, but if he/she denies knowledge of the situation, talk more generally about how pupils in the class get along and whether there are any problems. During this more wide-ranging chat, watch out for any suggestions that the victim is having problems. When these are raised, probe further.

Stage 2 Develop and reinforce a sense of common concern about the victim's difficulties

The key objective in this part of the session is getting the bully to agree that the situation is not good for xxxx. But, be careful here; don't get into a dispute about facts. The aim is to develop empathy with xxxx's position, who did or said what is not relevant.

Stage 3 Focus on solutions

The tutor now needs to get the bully thinking about changes that can be made which will help xxxx. The following words are suggested for this:

> We've talked long enough now. What do you suggest should be done?
>
> How can you help to improve things for xxxx?

When the pupil has come up with some positive ideas, move on to the next stage.

Stage 4 Arrange to meet in a week

A further, follow-up meeting should be held about a week later.
Say something like:

> That's good. We'll get together next week and you can tell me how you've been getting on.

[continued...]

17.1 Tutor Worksheet: Common Concern Method (continued)

Stage 5 Meet with the victim

Put the victim at his/her ease. Listen, be supportive and accept the victim's version. Then introduce the victim to some self-help ideas (see Section 16). Sometimes victims themselves can be provocative, if the tutor suspects this to be the case, it's important to discuss more acceptable ways of being popular with others. Perhaps some of the worksheets on friendship skills might be useful here (see Section 14).

Stage 6 Follow up

Probably the tutor will have to meet with the bully group on several occasions before a get-together can be arranged between the victim and the group. When the time is right, this meeting should be set up in the following way:

- The tutor should act as mediator.
- Explain the rules of discussion – everyone has a right to a viewpoint. Everyone has a right for his or her viewpoint to be listened to and respected.
- Ensure everyone is clear about what needs sorting out.
- Gather points of view from everyone involved.
- Look at everyone's needs in the situation.
- Draw up plans.
- Set up an agreement and make sure everyone has a copy.

The tutor should then keep a watchful eye to make sure that each pupil is following the agreement.

17.2 Tutor Worksheet: Dealing with Difficult Relationships

❖ *Arrange 4 chairs like this:*

❖ *Ask the pupil to sit on chair 1*

Say **"I want you to think about xxxx."**

What makes your relationship difficult?
Is it to do with the way you behave?
Is it to do with your skills or abilities at something?
Is it about the ideas you have?
Is it about who you are?
Is it about anything else?   *(Pause for answers after each question)*

❖ *Ask the pupil to now sit on chair 2*

Say **"Now I want you to imagine that you are not yourself, but xxxx. xxxx is thinking about you."**

Describe your thoughts.
Describe your feelings.
Describe your concerns.   *(Pause for answers after each question)*

❖ *Ask the pupil to now sit on chair 3*

Say **"You are now an outsider. You are thinking about *(pupil's name)* who you can see in chair 1, and xxxx who you can see in chair 2."**

What sort of relationship is this?
What do you think about these two people?
How do you feel about their relationship?
Can you see any need for change? What? Why? How?
   (Pause for answers after each question)

❖ *Ask the pupil to sit on chair 4*

Say **"You are a wiser person now."**

Look at yourself in chair 1.
Do you want to change anything?
Look at xxxx in chair 2.
Do you understand *(his/her)* thoughts, feelings, concerns?
Do you want to make any changes to your relationship? How?

17.3 Understand Yourself

Being truthful to yourself is an important first step in making any change. So reflect back. Have you ever tried to gain power over someone else by being aggressive or name-calling or by using indirect ways of bullying such as ignoring or passing around rumours?

If you have been involved in bullying behaviour, you may now realise that you have made a mistake. You might now want to change and improve your relationships with other people. To do this, you first need to understand yourself a bit more. Here's how to start.

Think about some of the **situations** where you have been involved in bullying someone else. What needs were you trying to satisfy? Was there a better way of satisfying those needs? Here are some suggestions. Fill in some ideas that would suit you.

Need	Better ways of satisfying this
I was trying to be powerful.	Find some situations where you can be a leader. For instance, start a club, join the school council. *My own ideas:*
I needed more attention from other people.	Look for situations that give you attention. For instance, join a drama group, a music group, a football team. *My own ideas:*
I was angry. I was trying to get my own back.	Work on a programme to manage your anger. (Your tutor will help you with this.) *My own ideas:*
I was in a mood.	Work on a programme to manage your feelings more effectively. (Your tutor will help you with this.) *My own ideas:*

Create a similar grid to help you to reflect back on any situations in which you have been involved.

17.4 Learn from Others

There will be people in your peer group who get on well with others and don't get involved in bullying. These are the people you need to study – you can learn a lot from them.

First, who are they? Write some of their names below.

_____   _____

_____   _____

_____

Now choose one person from your list who you particularly like and respect. Use that person as your **role model**. Over the next few weeks become a detective.

Find out how your role model:

✓ Agrees with friends on activities etc.

✓ Sorts out disagreements.

✓ Maintains his/her friendships.

Discuss your findings with your tutor and try to use the information to strengthen your own friendships in positive ways.

Finally ask your tutor to work through the **Friends** section of this unit with you. It will help you to understand some important ways of building new friendships and improving the ones you have already.

Section 18 Peer Pressure

Peer pressure can be a very positive thing. The right group of friends can encourage a young person in very helpful and constructive ways. But, as we all know, it can also lead some individuals into serious difficulties.

Because relationships with peers are so important, persuading a young person to resist peer pressure is a hard task. However, it often does need to be addressed, particularly in relation to school behaviour. The three worksheets in this section provide a starting point for this discussion. They could be used with individuals or with small groups.

Notes for Pupil Worksheets
(You may need to scribe for the pupil)

Peer Pressure – What is it? encourages students to think about both the positive and negative aspects of peer pressure. Spend some time discussing the pupil's responses and make sure that the concept of 'peer pressure' is fully understood before moving on.

Handling Peer Pressure is again a worksheet that requires in-depth discussion. If this worksheet is being used with a group, it could be useful to try out some role-plays to reinforce ideas. **Try it Out Yourself** gives further practice in countering negative pressures.

18.1 Peer Pressure – What is it?

Your peers are friends or acquaintances who are about the same age as you. They are the people who you interact with in lots of ways – at school, at home, in teams, at social occasions and so on. Peers influence your life in lots of ways because, as you spend time together, everyone listens and learns from each other.

Lots of the things you learn from your peers can be very **positive**. With their help you might become a better football player, dancer or artist. A friend might introduce you to a really exciting new book or computer game. A classmate might help you with your homework.

But peers can also influence each other in negative ways like playing up in class, truanting, stealing or drug-taking. Some of these, of course, are extreme things. Often peer influences can be negative in a more sneaky way – like suggesting that only the right sort of expensive trainers are acceptable; people that work hard at school aren't cool; or it's OK to pick on someone because 'everyone else does it'.

Of course you can just say "no" if someone tries to influence you to do something that you know is wrong. But often it's not that simple. People need to feel that they belong. They want to fit in with the group of people they like to hang around with, so sometimes they go along with things that make them feel uncomfortable. When this happens, it's called **negative peer pressure**.

Can you think of any recent examples of peer pressure that either you have personally experienced or known about? Were they positive or negative? Discuss them with your tutor and then try and give some examples in each column below.

Positive Peer Pressure	Negative Peer Pressure

18.2 Handling Peer Pressure

Here's a suggested routine for handling peer pressure.

1 Check out the situation

Are there any clues which suggest that someone is trying to pressurise you into doing something unacceptable? Here are some typical ones and their true meanings:

2 Listen to your inner voice

What is the voice inside your head telling you? Is what you're about to do right? Do you feel comfortable about this? Do you really want to do it?

3 Think about the consequences

Is someone going to get hurt if you do this? Think of the people you care about – how will it affect them? What will it do to you?

4 Decide how to act

Just saying "no" or leaving the situation is one choice. At times it might be the only possible one. But sometimes there are other more comfortable ways of rejecting something. You could:
- ❖ turn the suggestion into a joke as you say no;
- ❖ flatter the person who has asked you by saying something like "You're far too smart / nice / clever / ? / ? for that";
- ❖ suggest doing something more appropriate instead; or
- ❖ ignore the suggestion and change the subject.

18.3 Try it Out Yourself

Look at this situation. **Check** it out. **Listen** to your inner voice. Think about the **consequences**. Then decide how you would **act**.

Situation

> You're out with your friends. You've told your mum you'll be back at 9.30. At 9.15 you say you have to go. One friend says "It's too early to go home. Mick's having a party, let's go for a bit. Everyone will be there." Your other friend thinks it's a great idea. "Come on, tell your mum you missed the bus," she says, "otherwise you'll be the only one of our crowd who's not there."

Check (What are the pressures?)

_____

_____

Listen (Do you feel comfortable with the suggestion? Why?)

_____

_____

Think about the consequences (What will happen if you go?)

_____

_____

Act (What's the best way forward?)

_____

_____

Now try again with these situations:

❖ You're in a shop with your best friends. One of them picks up a pen and slips it into his pocket. The other laughs and pockets a set of pencils. "Your turn now," they both say.

❖ The bus is late. It's history today. You hate history lessons and you know that you'll be in trouble for not doing your homework. A couple of mates turn up and suggest skiving off round town. They say, "It's cool. We did it last week. No one found out."

Unit 5
Mood Management

Mood Management

Tutor Notes – Introduction

We all experience different moods and the very language we use illustrates this. Euphoric, depressed, happy, sad, anxious, exhilarated, angry, frightened and aggressive are all words describing mood states. Each of these emotional states can have levels and, if we experience a particular mood state regularly, we could probably rate it on a scale of 1 to 10.

Is there an ideal mood in which children learn well and behave appropriately in a school setting? We may not be able to answer this definitively, but we can say that certain moods will inhibit learning and certain moods undoubtedly affect behaviour in a detrimental way. Also some moods can affect health if they become prolonged.

There are, of course, reasons for the moods that we experience and we could classify the reasons into three categories.

1 Understandable: For instance, a person feeling sad when they have lost a loved one.

2 Physiological: For example, a person feeling anxious/angry when they are hungry due to the hormones, cortisol and adrenaline being released.

3 Thought determined: That is, moods brought about by thinking in a certain way.

It is the third category with which this section of the Toolkit is concerned.

'The way we think influences the way we feel'

In the 1960s Albert Ellis and Aaron T. Beck independently put forward this very simple but powerful thesis in the process of trying to treat patients suffering from depression. They knew from their work that successful people could, as a result of negative and catastrophic ways of thinking, perceive themselves as failures. The success of their treatment programmes rested on the premise that it is possible to change the way that we think and, in so doing, change the way we feel and act. Their ideas, and that of many other researchers since, have spread this concept to all areas of mood management. In fact, this simple thesis gave birth to a branch of cognitive psychology, which is the main theoretical basis of this mood management course.

However, just because something is simple in theory does not mean that it is easy to put into practice. We develop patterns of thinking that become so ingrained they are difficult to change. Psychological research has also shown that there is a genetic basis to personality and certain patterns of thinking can reflect personality types. Nevertheless, it is possible to change the way we think and this should be easier for younger people since their patterns of thinking will not be so set. Indeed, this is backed up by the more recent research of Martin Seligman and his co-workers. They have shown that although thought patterns in children can be used to predict later onset of depression, the same thought patterns could be changed to prevent such an outcome. For anyone who wants to do further reading on this subject, we would strongly recommend *Learned Optimism* by Martin Seligman.

Although this unit of the Behaviour Management Toolkit is entitled *Mood Management*, the moods principally covered relate to feeling depressed, having low self-esteem, feeling persecuted, etc. Anger is covered in more detail in Unit 3 *Anger Management*.

Working through this course once will not transform pessimists into optimists. Ways of thinking, even with young people, take a lot of changing. Tutors will need to see the pupil on a regular basis

to continually reinforce the need to challenge thinking patterns and to develop different ways of thinking. This may mean working through the relevant sections of this course many times.

Getting parents involved may also help. Parents can learn to pick out and challenge comments that indicate negative thinking patterns.

Structure of the Course

This unit is in four sections. The first (Section 19), **Hearing Your Inner Voice**, focuses on how thoughts influence mood and subsequent actions. Section 20 **Thinking, Feeling, Acting** and Section 21 **Manage That Mood** consolidate this concept and suggest a variety of ways by which negative thought patterns can be challenged, changed and managed. **Self-Esteem**, the subject of Section 22, is an area strongly related to mood management since poor self-esteem is well known to depress mood. This section makes further use of cognitive approaches to change the way the pupil is feeling and acting.

Section 19 Hearing Your Inner Voice

Notes for Pupil Worksheets
(You may need to scribe for the pupil)

Just Listen to Yourself! and **What's Going On?** introduce the pupil to the very simple idea that he or she has an inner voice. More importantly, it is possible to reflect on, and change, what that voice is saying and thus modify both feelings about, and outcomes of, a particular situation. This can be quite a dramatic revelation to a pupil and an in-depth understanding of these concepts can really empower him/her.

Your Inner Voice: What Does it Say? gives an example of how thinking in a particular manner can make someone feel resentful and cause them to act in unacceptable ways. The form at the bottom can be used to help the pupil to examine his/her own thoughts in a problem situation. Also, it may be useful at this point, to consider the problems that actually initiated involvement in this course.

Optimism and Pessimism introduces the idea that there can be a pattern to the way people think. Optimism often leads to an enhanced mood whilst pessimism in some cases results in a depressed mood, although it should be pointed out that this only applies to certain situations. For instance, if one were investing money, it may be better to be a little sceptical rather than overly optimistic.

It's Always Like This! shows how pessimistic thinking can lead to thinking in such a catastrophic way, that no solution to a problem can emerge. Watch out for words like "always" or "never" – they suggest no end to a problem. Similarly, using phrases which include "everything" or "nothing" imply that the problem is everywhere and there is no escape. People who think in these negative ways frequently also view themselves as victims of circumstance. "Everything always goes wrong for me"; "No one ever helps me." These are the sorts of phrases that can lead to a lowering of mood. The objective of this worksheet is to persuade students that a problem considered as a temporary difficulty will raise their mood and lead them to search out solutions. Spend some time discussing these ideas with the pupil before moving on.

19.1 Just Listen to Yourself!

We all talk to ourselves. It is a natural and normal thing to do. When you talk to yourself, this is called your **inner voice**.

Sometimes you can hear your inner voice clearly. Sometimes you are hardly aware of it. Try listening to your own inner voice. Is it telling you positive things or is it saying gloomy and depressing things? Discuss this with your tutor.

Here are some examples of the inner voice at work.

> Jane's teacher, Mr Smith, asks her a question. She realises that she doesn't know what he's talking about, because she's been busy thinking about the party she's going to on Friday. This is what Jane thinks:

> It's always like this. He always picks on me!
> I never get things right in his class.

> Asmir's teacher, Miss Jones, asks him a question. He realises that he doesn't know what she's talking about because he's been too busy thinking about football. This is what Asmir thinks:

> She's caught me out this time and she's not going to be very pleased. I'd better start paying attention instead of thinking about Saturday.

Whose inner voice gives the most positive picture of this situation, Jane's or Asmir's?

Why? What differences are there in the way Jane and Asmir think?

Discuss these questions with your tutor.

19.2 What's Going On?

When you have a problem, your thoughts about that problem affect the way you feel and how you deal with the problem.

Below you will find some examples of problems. Some of the thoughts, feelings and actions have been missed out. Can you fill them in?

Problem	Thought	Feeling	Action
Where's your homework? You know it was due in today!	Why does everyone always pick on me?	Resentful	She is rude to the teacher and gets two detentions.
Where's your homework? You know it was due in today!	Oh, I've forgotten to do it. Suppose I'll get a detention.		
I'm going to the cinema with Sami and Yasmin tonight. Sorry, they haven't invited you.	Good. I'll have time to write my essay and watch that video.	OK	That's fine. I've got loads of things to do tonight.
I'm going to the game with Rajeev and Dave tonight. Sorry, they haven't invited you.		Angry	

19.3 Your Inner Voice: What Does it Say?

Look at how Lewis's thoughts affect how he feels and what he does.

The problem:	Lewis's friends hid his shoes at the end of a PE lesson. This made him late for maths. Because he often arrives late, his maths teacher didn't believe his excuse and told him he'd have to stay behind at the end of the lesson to do some extra work.
Lewis's thoughts:	'She never believes anything I say. It's always the same. I'm always the one that gets picked on. It happens all the time. Teachers are always horrible to me. I hate this school.'
How Lewis felt:	Angry. Upset. Resentful.
What Lewis did:	Shouted at his teacher and rushed out of the room, slamming the door.

Over the next week, practise listening to your own **inner voice**. Notice how your inner voice talks to you when you come up against a problem. If you can, note one of these inner conversations down on the grid below. Then, in the next session, discuss it with your tutor.

The problem:	
My thoughts:	
How I felt:	
What I did:	

19.4 Optimism and Pessimism

Your **inner voice** is very important in many ways. For instance:

- ❖ It can make you feel **optimistic** (hopeful and confident).
- ❖ It can also make you feel **pessimistic** (gloomy and helpless).

Below, you can read the thoughts of two people. One is **Optimistic Oliver**; the other is **Pessimistic Paddy**. They have very different inner voices. Consider the situations below and read what Oliver's and Paddy's inner voices say to them.

Situations	Optimistic Oliver	Pessimistic Paddy
An advert for extras for a TV soap.	Sounds good. I think I'll have a go at that. Even if it doesn't work out it'll be fun.	I'll never get picked for something like that. It's not worth me trying. Who cares anyway?
An invitation to a party.	Great. I don't think I know anyone who'll be going, but I'm sure to meet some interesting people. Anyway, I know I'll have a good time.	It's sure to be boring, these things always are. I won't know anyone there, so I'll have no one to talk to.
A low score in a maths test.	I revised for it, but the questions were harder than I expected them to be. I think I need the teacher to re-explain some things. Well, it's only one test. I'll do better next time.	I must be thick. I revised really hard for this test but I always get things wrong. I'm just no good at maths. In fact I'm not much good at anything.

What differences did you notice between Optimistic Oliver and Pessimistic Paddy in the way that they talk to themselves? Discuss this with your tutor.

Very few people are always optimistic like Oliver or always pessimistic like Paddy. It's also not a question of optimism always being right and pessimism being wrong. Sometimes things happen that make us sad. Sometimes things happen that make us happy. Most people are a mixture of optimism and pessimism.

The important thing in any situation is to weigh up the facts accurately, to see the positive things as well as the negatives. Discuss this point with your tutor.

19.5 It's Always Like This!

❖ When you have a problem and your inner voice talks to you pessimistically, it begins to make you believe that the problem will never go away. If you think something is **permanent** (forever), then you believe that there is no point in trying to change it and you give up on it.

❖ On the other hand, if your inner voice tells you that the problem is just **temporary** (it can be changed, it's not forever), then you will search out ways to get rid of the problem.

❖ In the situations below and on the next sheet, some of the thoughts and feelings have been left out. Can you fill them in?

19.5 It's Always Like This! (continued)

Section 20 Thinking, Feeling, Acting

Notes for Pupil Worksheets
(You may need to scribe for the pupil)

Problems again emphasises the difference between 'permanent' thoughts and 'temporary' thoughts and the effect that each has on mood. Don't rush through this worksheet. Make sure the message is really understood.

Problems, Thoughts and Feelings is a crucial worksheet. It moves students from a theoretical appreciation of how thoughts influence mood towards a practical application of what they have learnt. Initially, quite a lot of support will be needed to help the pupil to analyse his/her thoughts and to fill in the grid. Continue to practise with further problems, until you feel satisfied that the student has thoroughly understood this approach.

Who's to Blame? When things go wrong some people never accept any responsibility for mistakes and these people are unlikely to suffer from depression since nothing is ever their fault. At the other extreme is the person who always seems to blame him/herself and the consequence of this self-blaming attitude is a lowering of mood that could lead to depression in the long-term. Clearly the ideal is a balanced view of what happens.

Who Do I Blame? enables the student to consider how he/she personally attributes blame when faced with problems. It also allows the pupil to examine the effect of thinking about mood from a personal standpoint.

Slicing the Pie is simply a technique for analysing a problem. **What am I Thinking?** extends this process by getting the pupil to analyse his/her thoughts in terms of permanence and blame.

Look for the Evidence, Challenge Those Negative Thoughts and **Acting Positively** are educational worksheets designed to make the pupil think about adversities in an analytical way rather than jumping to quick conclusions. After reading them together, the tutor and student will need to spend some time discussing these ideas. Several copies of **Get Practising** can then be run off so that the pupil can put into practice what has been learnt so far in this unit.

20.1 Problems

We all have problems and difficulties in life and we have already seen that how you think about these problems is important. Look at the inner voices of these two people.

Did you notice how this boy has used the words 'never' and 'forever'? These thoughts are telling him that his problems are **permanent** – they'll never be sorted out, so of course he's feeling down.

This girl's thoughts are telling her that her problems are only for now. They are just **temporary** and somehow things will be sorted. She's concerned but feels OK.

> If you have a problem and you think that it's **permanent**, you will feel negative (depressed, unhappy, angry) about life.
>
> If you have a problem and you think that it's only **temporary**, you'll generally feel OK. You know it will pass and you'll get over the difficulty.

Discuss this difference between **permanent** and **temporary** thoughts with your tutor. Make sure you understand the difference between them before you move on to the next worksheet.

20.2 Problems, Thoughts and Feelings

By working through the last few worksheets, you have learnt that the way you think about problems affects your feelings.

In this worksheet, your tutor will help you to focus on how you deal with your own difficulties.

On the grid below, describe a recent problem that you've had and then see if you can work out what your inner voice is telling you about this problem.

If your thoughts about the problem are **permanent** write them in that section. If your thoughts are **temporary** write them in the appropriate space for that.

Then write down the feelings and actions that resulted from these thoughts (their **consequences**).

Before you start, just make sure you have remembered the difference between permanent and temporary thoughts.

Problem	Who? What? When? Where?
Permanent Thought	
Consequent Feelings	
Temporary Thought	
Consequent Feelings	

It would now be a good idea to ask your tutor to make some more copies of this grid so you can try again with some other problems. In this way you'll discover for yourself how your thoughts affect the way you feel.

20.3 Who's to Blame?

When things go wrong, we can blame ourselves or we can think that someone or something else has caused the problem.

Look at the explanations in the grid below when Danny's team lost a football match. Who or what is getting the blame?

		Who or what is to blame?
	We lost because our goalie's no good. Then, Ben, who always thinks he's so marvellous, missed an easy penalty. The reason I didn't score was that no one was passing the ball my way. The ref was on the other side as well. So we had no chance.	
	We lost because the pitch was rubbish.	
	We lost because I just kept missing chances. It's always like this these days. I'm obviously not good enough for the team. I'll never be any good.	

Think about some recent things that haven't gone right for you. Who or what do you think was to blame for these problems? Discuss this with your tutor.

20.4 Who Do I Blame?

Remember: 'The way you think about a problem will affect the way you feel.' Once more, explain to your tutor what this means.

In this worksheet, you are again going to focus on your own problems. But this time you are going to think about who you **blame** for them and how this affects your feelings.

Describe a recent problem to your tutor. Then write it in the grid below.

Who do you blame for the problem? Yourself? Someone else? Something else?

If you blamed yourself, write your thoughts in the **'Because of me'** section.

If you blamed someone or something else, write your thoughts in the **'Because of someone/something else'** section.

When you have done that, underneath write down your **feelings** about the problem.

The Problem	Who? What? When? Where?
'Because of me'	
Thoughts	
Feelings	
'Because of someone/something else'	
Thoughts	
Feelings	

Suppose you changed your thoughts about who was to blame, would that have changed your feelings? Discuss this with your tutor.

Try this again with another problem. Can you see that who or what you blame for your problems also affects your feelings?

20.5 Slicing the Pie

Problems usually have a number of causes, but sometimes we get stuck in thinking that there is only one. Here's an example:

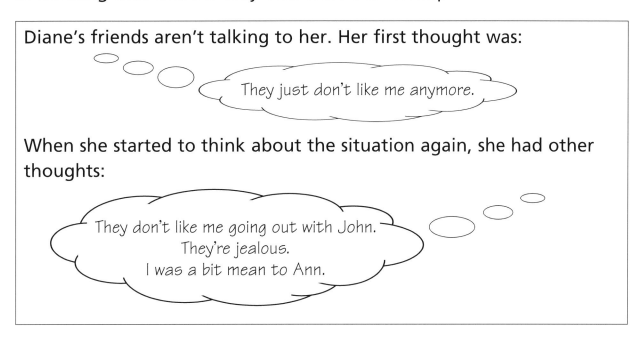

Imagine that the shape below is a pie, which has been cut into slices. Each slice represents a cause of the problem. So Diane's pie would look like this:

They don't like me anymore.	They don't like me going out with John.
They're jealous.	I was a bit mean to Ann.

Now try it for yourself.

Think of a problem that you've had. Now think of the things that might have caused this problem. Next draw a pie and slice it up. Finally, write one cause on each slice.

20.6 What am I Thinking?

You are now going to see if there is a pattern in how you think about problems. Are your thoughts 'permanent' or 'temporary'? Who do you blame? Yourself? Other people? Other things?

Start by looking back at the problem you 'sliced' in the last worksheet. With your tutor's help, see if you can write your thoughts into the sections on this grid. Some thoughts will be in more than one section.

Type of Thought	Thought
Permanent Thoughts (It always happens)	
Temporary Thoughts (Just this time)	
'Because of me' Thoughts	
'Because of someone/something else' Thoughts	

Can you see a pattern in the way you have been thinking about this problem? Discuss the results with your tutor.

Try this again with another problem.

20.7 Look for the Evidence

When things go wrong, we often believe the first thought that comes into our head.

But first thoughts can often be mistaken. When things do go wrong, it's important to look at all the possibilities. It's a bit like being a detective, you need to look at all the good and the bad possibilities and then weigh up the evidence.

So, when you have a problem:

❖ Don't accept your first thoughts about it.

❖ Look for other evidence.

❖ Consider everything carefully before you jump to conclusions.

This is called **challenging** your thoughts.

Here are three important things to remember.

1 The way you **think** about a **problem** affects how you **feel**.

2 By **challenging** your thoughts you can change the way you **think**.

3 By changing your thoughts you can alter the way you **feel**.

Explain each of these to your tutor. How could knowing these things improve the way in which you deal with problems?

20.8 Challenge Those Negative Thoughts

Tom wants to go on a weekend fishing trip with some friends. His dad isn't keen. He thinks that Tom is too young for this. He also wants Tom to catch up on some schoolwork. Tom is angry and rushes off to his room.

Tom's first thoughts are:

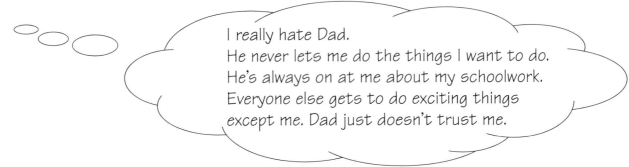

I really hate Dad.
He never lets me do the things I want to do.
He's always on at me about my schoolwork.
Everyone else gets to do exciting things except me. Dad just doesn't trust me.

But then he begins to **challenge** his first thoughts:

Hang on; I'm getting all upset and angry because I'm accepting the first things that come into my head. Let's look at the evidence.

Dad's OK really, he just worries about me. He lets me go ice-skating and to soccer matches with my mates. I suppose he's just worried about me going away with Andy and Johar for the whole weekend. He's right about me being behind with my homework.

I still feel a bit mad that I can't go but I don't hate Dad. Anyway Mike's mum won't let him go. Perhaps Mike can come round and keep me company this weekend.

Did you notice how Tom felt better after challenging his initial thoughts?

He stopped feeling so angry and began to plan for the future.

If you accept your first negative thoughts about a problem they'll make you feel bad and you won't have a reason to **act** positively.

So far, we have shown that by **challenging** your thoughts you can change the way you **think** and therefore change the way you **feel**.

But, we can now add another word. By **challenging** your thoughts, you can change the way you **think** and therefore change the way you **feel** and **act**.

20.9 Acting Positively

Challenging your negative thoughts will make you feel better. Instead of using up all your energy in feeling angry or depressed, you will have more 'get up and go' to do the things you enjoy. But learning to be good at challenging your thoughts takes practise, so here is an example to help you to understand how it works.

Jay's Story

Problem
My mum and dad have decided to split up.

Initial Thoughts
I hate them. They only think of themselves. They don't care about me.

Feeling and Acting
I feel really mad, but sad too. My friends know and have tried to help me, but I keep telling them to keep their noses out of my business. I'm short tempered at school, and that's getting me into trouble with my teachers.

Challenging that Negative Thinking
I don't really hate my mum and dad. I just want us to be a happy family like we used to be. They do care about me; otherwise they wouldn't worry about what's happening to me at school. I'm lucky to have good mates who want to help me. I usually get on OK at school. This has just been a rough patch and I know I can get through it.

Feeling and Acting
I feel a bit better now. I'm still unhappy about the break-up but I do know Mum and Dad both still love me and want the best for me. I'm going to talk to some of my friends about how I've been feeling. I think I'll also have a chat with my form teacher and explain what's been happening at home. I'm going to get on with doing the things I enjoy, instead of moping around.

Did you notice how challenging her thinking helped Jay to feel better?

It's easy to fall into the trap of accepting and acting upon your first thoughts and beliefs about problems. But if you want to move on, you must learn to weigh up the evidence for your beliefs and to challenge those that aren't supported by the facts of the situation.

20.10 Get Practising

Now it's time for you to put into practice what you have learnt. Think about a problem in your own life and write about it in the boxes below.

1 The problem
_____

2 My first thoughts about it
_____

3 My feelings
_____

4 Challenging my first thoughts

Evidence for them: _____
_____

Evidence against them: _____
_____

Other ways of looking at the problem: _____
_____

5 Challenging my thoughts has made me feel . . .
_____

I have decided to . . .
_____

Your tutor will make you some spare copies of this sheet so you can use them whenever new problem situations occur.

Section 21 Manage That Mood

Notes for Pupil Worksheets
(You may need to scribe for the pupil)

It's a Total Disaster is an educational worksheet that illustrates the effect of catastrophic thinking. So far in this unit the pupil has been shown the dangers of self-blame and making a problem into something permanent. This takes that a little further and shows how negative thinking can extend the problem to other areas of a person's life.

What Will Happen Next? describes a simple method of thinking that prevents a 'catastrophic approach', whilst **Get Practising** encourages a positive and practical way of thinking. **Try it Out for Yourself** allows the pupil to apply this technique to his/her own problems. Make some spare copies of this worksheet for future use.

21.1 It's a Total Disaster

So far we have been looking at problems that have **already happened** and learning how to view them more optimistically. But sometimes when bad things happen, we think that everything **in the future** is going to be terrible as well. Here's an example:

Can you see what Jason is doing? Yes, he has had a setback. But he's telling himself that as a result of this, everything else in his life is going to be a disaster.

People often turn setbacks into disasters. When something bad happens, they start to think of all the really terrible things that could happen next. Then they really begin to believe their thoughts and their whole future seems to look terrible. In this way, a small setback can turn into a **catastrophe**.

21.2 What Will Happen Next?

When you have a setback, it's natural to think about how this will affect your future. But it's important not to end up believing that even worse things will happen next. So when you have a problem, you need to ask yourself these three questions:

1 What is the worst thing that could happen now?
2 What is the best thing that could happen now?
3 What is most likely to happen?

Obviously, you will want the best thing to happen, so your next step is to work out a plan. You will need to decide what to do to prevent the worst thing from happening and what to do to get the best result. This is called **taking control**. Look at this example. It will help you to see how to take control after a setback.

Situation

Anna borrows her sister Helen's new leather jacket without asking permission. She wears it to a party. Some of Anna's friends admire it, so they all try it on. As they are doing this, the lining, somehow, gets torn.

What will happen next?

What is the worst thing that could happen? Helen will be so angry she will never trust Anna again.
What can be done to prevent the worst thing happening? Anna could own up about the situation as soon as possible and offer to pay for the jacket to be repaired.

What is the best thing that could happen? Helen will not be angry, but just accept the situation.
What can be done to help the best thing to happen? Anna could apologise for her behaviour and offer to give something of her own to Helen.

What is most likely to happen? Helen will be angry for a while. It will take time for Anna to earn her trust again.
If the most likely thing does happen, how should Anna deal with it? She should accept Helen's anger and try to find ways to make up for her own bad behaviour.

21.3 Get Practising

Here are some more situations for you to practise on. For each one, try and work out:

- ❖ What is the worst thing that could happen?
- ❖ What could stop the worst thing happening?

- ❖ What is the best thing that could happen?
- ❖ What could help the best thing to happen?

- ❖ What is most likely to happen?
- ❖ What is the best way to handle this if it does happen?

At lunchtime, Marcus was given permission to work on his project in the woodwork room. He sees his friends outside, opens the window and tells them to come in and join him. They come in and start messing about. Another boy's project is pushed off the bench and a computer monitor screen is broken.

What happens next?

Sian meets her friend Nicola at the bus stop. Nicola persuades Sian not to go to school, but to go back to her house for the day because her parents are out at work. They spend the morning playing records and trying on clothes. School rings Sian's mum to find out why she isn't at school.

What happens next?

Sam's friends are going to the pictures. Sam's mum won't give him any money to go. She says he has to stay in and revise for a test the next day. Sam takes some money from his mum's purse and goes off with his friends.

What happens next?

21.4 Try it Out for Yourself

When you next have a problem, use the 'What happens next?' approach. This worksheet will help you to do this, so it would be a good idea to keep a copy handy.

This is the situation:	
This is the worst possible outcome:	This is the best possible outcome:
One thing I can do to prevent the worst thing from happening:	One thing I can do to help make the best thing happen:
The most likely outcome:	
How should I handle the most likely outcome if it does happen?	

Section 22 Self-Esteem

Note: This section could just as easily be put into Unit 4 Peer Relationships, *since it fits well into both units. Being able to make and keep friends particularly helps self-esteem, so we suggest that tutors should use Section 14* **Friends** *to help their students in this respect.*

The importance of self-esteem cannot be over emphasised. Children growing up developing a sense of poor self-esteem are more likely to go into depression in later life. Even if clinical depression does not occur, low self-esteem can lead to an unhappy life.

Notes for Pupil Worksheets (You may need to scribe for the pupil)

The worksheet **Value Yourself** introduces the pupil to the concept of self-esteem and how it is affected by the way he or she thinks.

Meet Jenny and **Meet Ben** both illustrate how people's self-esteem is affected by the way they think. The idea of challenging negative thoughts is also introduced.

Self-evaluation starts with **This is Me!** and **Strengthen Your Strengths and Set Some Goals**. You should notice that the focus is on the student's good qualities. Gentle encouragement may be needed to emphasise strengths and to deter the pupil from introducing negative ideas.

Challenge Your Negative Thoughts and **Thought Challenging Sheet** lead the pupil through the best ways of combating a low self-esteem. It is particularly important that these sheets are used again and again to the point that challenging negative thoughts and setting personal targets become habits.

22.1 Value Yourself

People who feel happy with themselves are more likely to have good relationships with others. Happy people are also better at recognising their own skills and abilities and good at acknowledging other people's talents. People who feel content with themselves are less likely to want to control and dominate others.

So, if you want to feel good about others, you need to feel good about yourself. This is called **self-esteem**. The next few worksheets are about self-esteem, but before you start work on them, try looking up some meanings of the word 'esteem' in the dictionary.

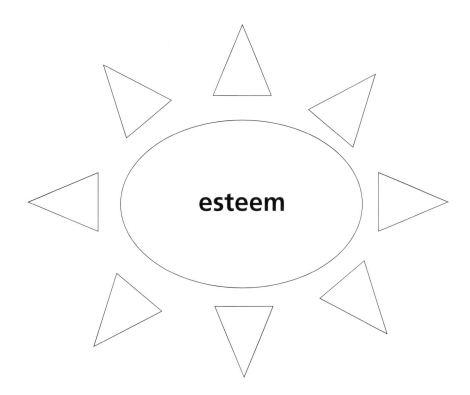

Now you understand the word 'esteem', write down what you think 'self-esteem' means:

_____

_____

22.2 Meet Jenny

Jenny has high self-esteem. She always encourages herself by thinking positively about things. Even when something goes a bit wrong, Jenny tells herself that she'll be able to sort it out.

Below are some of Jenny's thoughts and feelings. Fill in the last column with your own ideas of how her thoughts and feelings might make Jenny act.

Thoughts	Feelings	Actions
I like being in this group.	Relaxed Confident Comfortable	Works hard. Gets on with others. Respects the rules.
People said I looked smart in my new top.	Satisfied Pleased Contented	
I've got some good mates. We get on well together.	Accepted Fitting in Belonging	
I only got 6 in that maths test, but tomorrow I'm going to try and get 8.	Determined Optimistic Strong-minded	
I've sorted out what I was doing wrong, so I'll be OK next time.	Confident Positive Upbeat	

22.3 Meet Ben

People with high self-esteem feel secure, confident, accepted and positive. They are also determined to set their own goals and sort out their own problems.

These are the building blocks of self-esteem. Nobody feels *all* of these things *all* the time. Everyone has times when they feel worried or a bit down. But it's important to understand that you don't have to stay that way. You can build yourself back up by **thinking the right way**.

Meet Ben and read his thoughts

Now let's challenge his thoughts. Let's give him some new positive thoughts and see how he feels then. By doing this we can build up his self-esteem. Fill in the incomplete and empty boxes with your own ideas.

Ben's thoughts	His feelings	New thoughts	New feelings
I'm ugly.	embarrassed	I looked good when I wore …………………	
I always get left out.	lonely	Remember the time I joined in ………………	
I always do things wrong. I'm just thick.	helpless	I did alright ………………	
Teachers always pick on me.	angry		

22.4 This is Me!

This worksheet will help to highlight some of the positive things about you.

Let's start with your **personal qualities**. Put a circle round any of the words below that describe you well and add any others you can think of.

caring   amusing   interesting   calm   successful   popular   kind
exciting   gentle   generous   loyal   funny   careful   affectionate
reliable   well-organised   good tempered   happy   lovable
hard-working   relaxed   compassionate   thoughtful   clever   likable
polite   generous   helpful   _____ ?
_____ ?   _____ ?   _____ ?

Now write down some of your special **skills** and **talents**.

_____
_____
_____

Next, make a list of some of your **recent successes** and **achievements**.

_____
_____
_____

Who are the **special people** in your life? Write their names below.

_____
_____

Finally, write down some of the things you want to achieve. Make sure your goals are realistic.

_____
_____
_____

22.5 Strengthen Your Strengths and Set Some Goals

Re-read the last worksheet 'This is Me!' and then write some **really positive** sentences about yourself.

Examples: I am a really good friend to...
People like me because I...
I'm great at...

_____
_____
_____
_____

Positive sentences about yourself are called **affirmations**.

Find a piece of card and copy down your affirmations. Keep your affirmation card in a place where you can easily get it out and look at it. Read the card at least three times each day for the next four weeks. Try and learn your affirmations and say them over to yourself whenever you can.

Now you know some of the good things about yourself, develop them further by setting yourself some **goals**. Remember to make your goals realistic or you won't achieve them.

Examples: This week, I'm going to find out about joining...
Over the next three weeks I am going to strengthen my skills as a good friend by really listening to...
Over the next month I am going to really work at...

Now you try some:

_____
_____
_____
_____

22.6 Challenge Your Negative Thoughts

We all get negative thoughts from time to time, but if you want to be happy and to feel good about yourself, you mustn't let these thoughts take you over. You have to learn to challenge them. Here's how to do it.

1 Write down your negative thought and the feeling this gives you.
2 Measure the strength of your feeling by giving it a number between 1 (weak) and 10 (very strong).
3 Challenge your negative thought. Replace it with a more positive one.
4 Measure the strength of the feeling again.
5 Challenge again with another positive thought.
6 Keep doing this until you have lowered the strength of your feeling.

Here's an example to help you to understand this process.

- Rob doesn't like school. Monday mornings are particularly difficult for him.
- He thinks: 'I hate school. This week is going to go so slowly. I'll never get through it.'

- This makes him feel upset.
- He measures his 'upset' feeling. It's very strong. He gives it 9.

1	2	3	4	5	6	7	8	9	10
weak				strong				very strong	

- He challenges his first thought with this one: 'Actually, today won't be too bad. I've got PE first lesson.'

- Now when he measures how upset he is, he finds he's on 6 (strong).

- He tries again with more thoughts like these: 'Lunchtime will be OK, I'll play football with Alex and Kev. We've got science this afternoon. I enjoy doing the experiments.'

- He measures the strength of his feeling after each new thought and finally gets his upset feeling down to 2. Rob is now able to cope with his day.

22.7 Thought Challenging Sheet

Make a few copies of this sheet and use it whenever you want to rid yourself of unwanted thoughts and feelings.

Thought:
Feeling:
How strong? 1____2____3____4____5____6____7____8____9____10 weak　　　　　　　strong　　　　　　very strong
Challenging thought:
How strong is the feeling now? 1____2____3____4____5____6____7____8____9____10 weak　　　　　　　strong　　　　　　very strong
Challenging thought:
How strong is the feeling now? 1____2____3____4____5____6____7____8____9____10 weak　　　　　　　strong　　　　　　very strong
I feel OK now because...

22.8 Body Talk

Have you ever heard someone say "She looks down today"?

It's used when someone looks fed up or depressed.

When people are sad or depressed, they really do look down.

- ❖ Their eyes tend to look towards the ground.
- ❖ Their mouths are turned down.
- ❖ Their shoulders are hunched.
- ❖ They even walk more slowly!

Demonstrate some depressed 'body talk' to your tutor.

How does it make you feel?

Depressed body talk keeps you feeling down, so don't accept it.

Challenge it!

Next time you feel low:

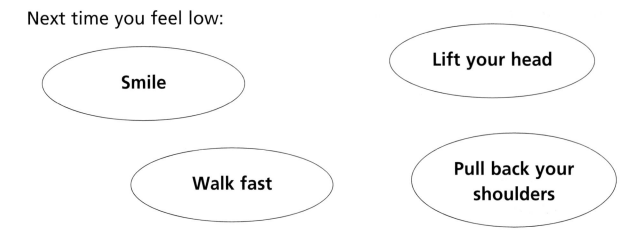

Try this out with your tutor. Notice how you feel when you do this.

Bibliography and References

Many books and papers have influenced our ideas in relation to behaviour management. Unfortunately, it is only possible to mention some of the most significant ones here. Those that we consider to be of particular importance, and would recommend as further reading, have been starred.

Bandler, Richard & Grindler, John (1979) *Frogs into Princes – Neuro Linguistic Programming*, Eden Grove Editions.

Cowan, David, Palomares, Susanna & Schilling, Dianne (1994) *Conflict Resolution for Teens*, Interchoice Publishing.

Donnellan, Craig (ed) (1998) *Issues*. Bullying, Volume 13, Independence Educational Publishers.

Focal Point Audio Visual Ltd. Hand-Out Material on *Understanding, Controlling and Preventing Anger*.

Gentry, W. Doyle (1999) *Anger-Free – Ten basic steps to managing your anger*, Quill, HarperCollins.

Glasser, William (1965) *Reality Therapy*, Harper & Roe.

*Glasser, William (1998) *Choice Theory*, Harper Perennial.

Goldstein, Arnold P., Glick, B. & Gibbs, J. (1998) *Aggression Replacement Training*, Research Press.

*Goleman, Daniel (1995) *Emotional Intelligence*, Bantam Books.

*Greenberger, Dennis & Padesky, Christine A. (1995) *Mind Over Mood; Change How You Feel by Changing the Way You Think*, The Guilford Press.

Hemphill, Sheryl A. & Littlefield, L. (2001) *Evaluation of short term group therapy program for children with behaviour problems and their parents*. Behaviour Research and Therapy 39: 823–841.

Jasmine, Julia (1997) *Conflict Resolution*, Teacher Created Materials Inc.

Matthews, Andrew (1990) *Making Friends*, Media Masters.

Modrcin-McCarthy, Mary Anne & Barnes, Flannery B. (1998) *Childhood Anger: So common, yet so misunderstood*, Journal of Child and Adolescent Psychiatric Nursing 11: 2: 69–77.

Munro, Sheila (1997) *Overcoming Bullying*, Piccadilly.

*O'Connor, Joseph (2001) *NLP Workbook – The practical guide to achieving the results you want*, Thorsons.

Pikas, Anatol (1989) *The Common Concern Method for the Treatment of Mobbing*. Chapter 8 of "Bullying: An International Perspective" Edited by Roland, E. & Munthe, E., David Fulton.

Pinel, John P. (2003) *Biopsychology*, 5th Edition, Allyn & Bacon.

Reeder, Darcy M. (1991) *Cognitive Therapy of Anger Management: Theoretical and Practical Considerations*, Archives of Psychiatric Nursing 5: 3: 147–150.

*Seligman, Martin E. P. (1991) *Learned Optimism*, Pocket Books.

Seligman, Martin E. P. (1995) *The Optimistic Child*, Harper Perennial.

Rose, Sheldon D. (1998) *Group Therapy With Troubled Youth*, Sage Publications.

Taylor, Ted K., Eddy, J. Mark & Biglan, Anthony (1999) *Interpersonal skills training to reduce aggressive and delinquent behavior: Limited evidence and the need for an evidence-based system of care*, Clinical Child and Family Psychology Review 2: 3: 169–182.

Waxman, David (1989) *Hartland's Medical & Dental Hypnosis*, Baillière Tindall.

Yarcheski, Adela, Mahon, Noreen E. & Yarcheski, Thomas J. (1999) *An empirical test of alternate theories of anger in early adolescence*, Nursing Research 48: 6: 317–323.